Westwood, Jennifer.
    Gilgamesh & other Babylonian tales.
Drawings by Michael Charlton. [1st American ed.] Coward-McCann [1970, c1968]
    96 p. illus., map. 4.95

    Adaptations of Babylonian tales.

1.Tales, Babylonian. 2.Folklore, Babylonian.

18149   My 74

19

About the Book

The stories in this collection are among the oldest known to mankind. They were first told by the Sumerians, the inventors of the written word. When the Sumerian civilization collapsed just before 2000 B.C., their writing, language, and much of their mythology were taken over by the Babylonians, who lived in southern Mesopotamia. The Sumerian stories, with Babylonian modifications and additions, were preserved in Babylonian libraries of clay tablets.

The principal story in the volume, "Gilgamesh," is man's first known heroic epic. It tells of the mighty deeds of Gilgamesh, King of Uruk, his friendship with Enkidu, and his search for eternal life.

Two of the other tales — the story of the Creation and the story of the Flood — bear a startling resemblance to the accounts found in the Bible's Book of Genesis. Interesting differences and similarities can be noted.

Jennifer Westwood has the rare ability to retell myths in a lively readable style, while still preserving the flavor of the original text. GILGAMESH AND OTHER BABYLONIAN TALES will appeal not only to archeologists and other scholars, but also to any reader who enjoys a good story.

GILGAMESH
& Other Babylonian Tales

JENNIFER WESTWOOD

Drawings by
MICHAEL CHARLTON

COWARD-McCANN
NEW YORK

This book is for my parents

6-27-74
C52

First American Edition 1970
© 1968 by Jennifer Westwood
Illustrations © 1968 by The Bodley Head

Library of Congress Catalog Card Number: 71-105576

Contents

Introduction

In ancient times, Iraq was the homeland of two nations mentioned in the Bible, the Babylonians and the Assyrians. We give the name Babylonia to the territory stretching from modern Baghdad to the Persian Gulf, Assyria to Iraq north of Baghdad. They were both Akkadian peoples, speaking a language called Akkadian. This itself belonged to the Semitic family of languages, which includes Hebrew. You will not be surprised, therefore, when you find that legends told among the Babylonian people were preserved in Assyrian libraries and even found their way into Canaan with the Hebrews!

The Babylonians did not invent the stories which you will read. Before Babylonia and Assyria took shape, there was a kingdom on the Persian Gulf called Sumer. To this day, we do not know who its inhabitants, the Sumerians, were, for their language is related to no other, living or dead. They seem to have entered Southern Iraq in about 4000 BC, and their coming marked the beginning of a struggle with the Semitic peoples already there, which lasted for 2000 years. At first, the Sumerians were victorious and were able to establish the city-states

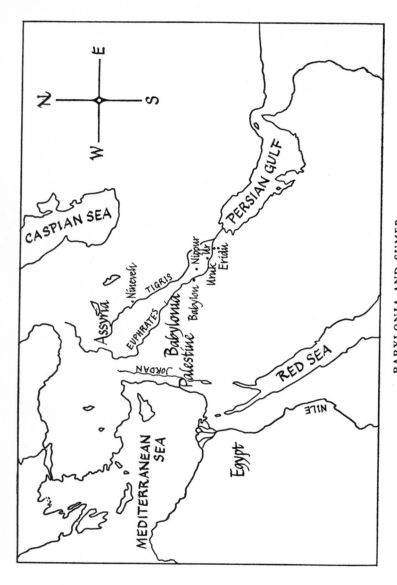

BABYLONIA AND SUMER

In the Ancient World the Persian Gulf extended further north than it does to-day. Ur and Eridu were seaports.

which made up the kingdom of Sumer. As in Ancient Greece, each city had its own king and its own god, and now one city, now another, predominated over the rest. Sumer flourished and became very important. The Sumerians were probably the inventors of the cuneiform ('wedge-shaped') system of writing which was soon adopted by their illiterate neighbours, so that by about 2000 BC it had spread throughout the Near East. But the Semitic people were gathering strength and in about 2050 BC, they finally overthrew the Sumerians, destroying their last capital, Ur. In about the fourteenth century BC, the Akkadians living north of Sumer established Babylon as their capital city, took control of the whole area between Baghdad and the Persian Gulf, including Sumer itself, and thus created Babylonia.

The Heroic Age of any nation is a time in the past when a certain way of living was in progress. This usually involved government by petty kings, who perhaps ruled no more than one city or tribe, and who were maintained in power by their armies, in particular by the royal bodyguards who formed a sort of military aristocracy. A pantheon of gods was worshipped, the deities being pictured as men and women and organised as a family. The literature would consist for the most part of narrative poems, intended for recitation or singing and concerned primarily with the deeds of heroes. At some stage after the Heroic Age, all the separate stories about one hero might be gathered together and used to make one long poem, called an epic, which related all that was known of his life. From the Heroic Age of Greece came the material for the *Odyssey* of Homer, from that of Northern Europe came the substance of *Beowulf*, written by some Anglo-Saxon long after his tribe had migrated from the districts of Scandinavia in which the poem has its setting. The Sumerians, too, had their Heroic Age, and during this time there arose, side by side with the religious myths, the tales of human heroes such as Gilgamesh, Utnapishtim and Adapa, who may have been historical kings.

It is lucky for us that when the Babylonians becamedomina nt they did not wipe out the Sumerian civilisation but took it over. Otherwise, though archaeologists might find the ancient cities of Sumer, they would not be able to put a name to them, or tell us much about what the Sumerians believed and thought, which is much more interesting than what sort of cooking-pots they used! Luckily, the Babylonians saw fit to preserve the Sumerian language and they used it as their language of religion, much as Latin was used by the Church in mediaeval Europe. Together with the language, they took over the gods, the mythology and the hero-legends. Indeed, most of the Sumerian texts which have been found by archaeologists, were actually written down by Babylonians when Sumerian was already a dead language although the contents were probably composed much earlier. Sometimes the Babylonians altered things here and there to suit themselves, for example giving to their own god Marduk the myths that had belonged to Enlil. So we cannot really talk of Sumerian or Babylonian myths and legends, but to be accurate should call them something like Sumero-Babylonian. This is so clumsy, however, that most people simply speak of Babylonian myths and legends, bearing in mind that many of these are of Sumerian origin. We must also remember that some legends, such as that of Gilgamesh, are known to us in their present form from texts inscribed in Assyria.

We must be grateful to the Babylonians, not only for preserving Sumerian beliefs, but also for enabling us to decipher the Sumerian language. The name 'Sumer' is not mentioned in the Bible or in any other ancient record, and the kingdom had been forgotten completely until about a hundred years ago, when archaeologists began to excavate sites in Iraq, looking for the Babylonians and Assyrians who *were* remembered. Fortunately, none of these peoples wrote on paper, which would have crumbled to dust long ago, but on baked clay tablets which stood a good chance of surviving centuries of burial in the ruins of their libraries. At first, people did not realise that these tablets were 'books'. When they did, and when they had unearthed tablets inscribed in Akkadian by the Babylonians and Assyrians, they were able to decipher the language by comparing it to other languages of the Semitic group. When tablets written in Sumerian came to light, they were faced with a seemingly impossible task. How could they understand a language which was like no other the world had ever seen? But the Babylonians came to the rescue—their scribes had made some bilingual texts in Akkadian and Sumerian, and also dictionaries of a sort, to help them learn their language of religion. They little dreamt that one day their 'cribs' were to help the discoverers of a lost race. For, once Akkadian was understood, Sumerian could be deciphered. Of course, there are still many words which cannot be translated; many stories survive only in fragments, with vital parts lost; many more tablets may still be buried in Iraq and may never be excavated. But although we have only a few myths and legends which are more or less complete, they are enough to show us that the Sumerians and Babylonians were great poets. More stories may one day be found, but it is difficult to imagine that they could be more moving or compelling than the stories of Gilgamesh or of the Flood.

All the stories in this book were written on clay tablets in

Akkadian, except for *Inanna in the Underworld* which is in Sumerian. Many of the actual tablets can be seen in the Room of Writing, in the British Museum. Also in the British Museum, in the Department of Western Asiatic Antiquities, are objects excavated from Babylonian and Sumerian cities. Some of these things are very beautiful, such as the harp from the grave of a queen of Ur. If you look closely at this, you will see that it carries a picture of Gilgamesh!

1. Marduk and Tiamat

This story is contained in a Babylonian poem known from its opening words as Enuma elish *('When on high'). Enuma elish, which was recited twice during the great Babylonian New Year Festival, was first and foremost written in honour of the god Marduk, who became the national god of Babylonia during the First Babylonian Dynasty (1894-1595 BC), replacing Enlil as the chief god. The poem was probably composed during that period as a piece of religious and political propaganda for the city of Babylon. Surely the city which was built by the gods for Marduk, the creator of men and king of the gods, was worthy of the leadership it was claiming?*

The first fragment of Enuma elish *to be discovered, came from the library of King Ashurbanipal, the king of Assyria in the seventh century BC. When the civilisation of the Sumerians was eclipsed, their poems passed into the hands of the Babylonians. When in turn Babylonia dwindled in importance, the poems were again passed on, this time to the rising kingdom of Assyria. Ashurbanipal, the last great Assyrian king, was a collector of literary documents, as well as an outstanding soldier, and he sent servants to examine the archives of the ancient cities of Babylonia, and to translate texts from Sumerian into his own Assyrian dialect. The* Epic of Gilgamesh, Enuma elish *and* Adapa and the South Wind *are some of the poems preserved by Ashurbanipal's librarians at Nineveh, the Assyrian capital. Unfortunately, a combined army of Medes and Babylonians destroyed Nineveh in 612 BC. The library fell in ruins and all its 'books' were lost until, centuries later in 1839, Austin Henry Layard began to* excavate the site of the ancient city. He brought back to the British Museum thousands of broken clay tablets which he had found buried there. The excavations continued and more tablets were unearthed, but it was not immediately realised that these were written documents and they were not deciphered for a number of years. When the art of reading cuneiform was finally discovered, many revelations were in store, as you will see from the introductions to The Story of the Flood and Gilgamesh. In its full form, Enuma elish shows many similarities to the Book of Genesis, and is an example of the close contact between Hebrew and Babylonian mythology.

Some parts of Marduk and Tiamat may be a little difficult to understand unless you bear in mind that at one level Apsu and Tiamat and their children are gods in human form, but at the other they are primeval forces engaged in the process of evolution. At this level, the mingling of the salt-water with the sweet-water ocean produced first mist (Mummu), then matter (Lahmu and Lahamu, Anshar and Kishar). It used to be said that Tiamat was a dragon, but there is not enough evidence to support this. If you see her as a woman when she does something woman-like, and as an ocean when she does something ocean-like, there will be no muddle. There is a difference between Apsu and 'the Apsu'. The first is an ocean and a god; the second is the home of Ea, made from the waters of Apsu when he has been overcome by Ea. The Babylonians believed that all fresh water on the surface of the earth originated in the Apsu, the waters on which the earth floated. The Apsu itself and the sweet-waters on the earth were in the charge of Ea; the earth and the air above it belonged to Enlil; Heaven, which lay beyond the air, was ruled by Anu.

WHEN on high the heavens had not been made and the firm ground below was not created, in the emptiness of Chaos Apsu dwelled, the ocean of sweet-water. With him in the void was Tiamat, the great salt-water ocean and his wife. Mummu, their son, was with them. In those times, none of the race of gods had yet been born. Then, where the salt and the sweet waters mingled, within them were created first Lahmu and Lahamu, one male, the other female. Before these were fully-grown the waters spawned another pair, Anshar and Kishar, who surpassed the others both in stature and in might; yet Anu, Anshar's first-born, equalled him. Anu created Ea, the all-wise, in his own image. He created him the master of all wisdom and more strong than any of his elders.

Time went by, and other gods were made. They exulted in their power and there arose the shouting of the young gods filled with pride. There was singing where they were, and Apsu could not rest in peace nor make them hold their tongues. And so he called for Mummu, and the two discussed with Tiamat the irksome matter. Apsu spoke in rage: 'I have no rest by day or night. I cannot sleep. I shall destroy them *and* their singing!'

But Tiamat exclaimed: 'What? Should we now destroy what we have made? They cause us grief perhaps, but yet forbear, for they are our own sons!'

Then Mummu spoke, and his designs were dark.

'Destroy them all! Peace will return again. You will have rest by day and night. O Apsu, you will sleep!'

When Apsu heard this, he was glad at heart. His face grew bright at the evil that he planned. Mummu embraced his neck, sat on his knee, and whispered in his ear what they should do.

But Ea, who knew all things, learned their plan, and he devised a spell that could not fail. He caused a deep enchantment to float out upon the waters, he poured heavy sleep upon the ancient Apsu, so that he could not wake; and Mummu slumbered with him. While both were wrapped in sleep, Ea came and bound them. He cut through Apsu's sinews, tore off the Crown of Splendour, set it on his own head, and then slew the dreaming god. He set Mummu in prison, binding him for ever with a cord tied through his nose, but Tiamat he spared.

Ea built a chamber upon the back of Apsu; in the middle of the waters he made his dwelling-place, naming it the Apsu, and he lived there with his wife. And there the wisest of the wise, the wisest of the gods, was born—Marduk, Son of the Sun, the Sun-god of the Gods. When Ea saw him, he rejoiced and on his new-born son bestowed a double godhead, so that he surpassed all other gods in power. When his lips moved, fire blazed forth, and round his head there shone the fearful light of majesty. For him, Lord Anu made the winds, the North and South, the East and West, as weapons to his growing hand. But with them he caused waves, and this disturbed great Tiamat; she grew sullen and unquiet.

When they saw that she was restless, her first-born children came to her. They were the spirits of the void, made before Anshar's line. They said: 'When they slew Apsu, *you* looked on and did not trouble. Now they have made you restless. Will you now lift your hand against these thieves of quietness? As for us, our eyes are heavy. We long for sleep but find none, for you move ceaselessly and on your breast we cannot slumber. Come with us. We shall give them up to storm, and take revenge for Apsu, at the same time winning rest.'

These first-born gods, who lived with her, were angry and they plotted. Tiamat fashioned monsters to fight against the rest—the Viper and the Dragon, the Sphinx and the Great Lion, the Mad Dog and the Scorpion-man, Demons of the Storm, the Dragonfly and Bison; in all they were eleven. From among her elder children who took her part against the young, she exalted one called Kingu, and to him she gave dominion and the high command of battle. She fastened on his breast the magic tablets which rule fate. Tiamat said to Kingu: 'Your command must be obeyed; what you ordain must come to pass. Your decree is now as binding as the decree of Anu.'

Thus she arrayed her troops and planned to slay her younger sons, to avenge the death of Apsu.

But Ea, who knew all things, learned her counsels; he fell silent, and brooded deep within himself, both angry and afraid. The days grew long, but when at last his anger had subsided, he made his way to Anshar and revealed all that had passed.

'Our mother, Tiamat, has summoned up a host, and all the gods have turned to her, except the ones you made. They are angry and they plot both by daytime and by night-time. Tiamat has made monsters to fight against your line—the Viper and the Dragon, the Sphinx and the Great Lion, the Mad Dog and the Scorpion-man, Demons of the Storm, the Dragonfly and Bison—in all they are eleven. From among her elder children who take her part against the young, she has exalted Kingu; she has given him dominion and the high command of battle. She has fastened on his breast the tablets which rule fate. She has equalled him to Anu!'

When Anshar heard all this, he smote his thigh and bit his lip, for he was much perplexed. He grew gloomy. He grew restless. He groaned and pleaded: 'Ea! You slew the ancient Apsu. You must strike down Tiamat.'

Ea went and saw, and soon returned. Then Anshar turned to Anu: 'She comes on unopposed! Go, Anu. Bid her cease. If your command is not enough, then give her mine and she will halt.'

Anu obeyed. He went to her and bade her halt, but still she came. He turned and fled.

'I am afraid,' was all that he could say.

Again Anshar fell silent. He looked first at the ground, and then looked up and shook his head at Ea, but no plan was offered by the wise one. The young gods all assembled. They did not speak, their lips were closed, till one groaned: 'What are we to do? No god can fight with Tiamat and live!'

Their father, Anshar, sat and pondered. Then, at last, he said: 'Yet hope is left to us. There *is* one whose strength is such that he may save us all. He shall avenge the fear of Ea; he shall avenge the fear of Anu. The valiant Marduk will defend us.'

Ea went to fetch his son, and gave him this advice: 'Go straight to Anshar, fully armed and ready for battle. Stand forth and speak out boldly. Offer him your aid. His heart will lighten when he sees you.'

Marduk did as he was told. When Anshar saw him come, his heart grew light again with hope. The young god asked: 'What would you have me do? What man has stirred up war with you?'

'It is Tiamat, a woman, who has stirred up war against us. I sent Ea out, and Anu, but they returned afraid.'

'Soon, Anshar, you shall set your foot upon her neck,' said Marduk.

Anshar answered, 'Will you drive out in your Chariot of Storm?'

'If I do this,' said Marduk, 'you must call the gods together, and in their presence give me power above all other gods, so that my decrees are binding, what I say is, and whatsoever I create shall not be changed. Let me determine fate.'

Anshar called his messenger: 'Go to Lahmu and Lahamu. Summon them to feast with me. Tell them that Tiamat has raised up war against us; that first I sent out Ea, but that he returned afraid; that next I sent out Anu, but that he came back trembling; that Marduk, the young hero, then came forward with brave heart and said that, if he slew her, I must call the gods together and in their presence give him power above all other gods, so that his decrees are binding, what he says is, and whatsoever he creates shall not be changed. He must determine fate. Tell them that they must come quickly and confer this power upon him. Go, messenger, and say this.'

When at last the messenger reached Lahmu and Lahamu, he told them word for word everything that Anshar said. Together they set out and soon reached Anshar. In the meantime, a feast had been prepared for them. The gods all ate, and drank sweet wine to soothe their cares away. Then Marduk was called forth. The gods built him a lordly throne and, when he took his place to receive the kingship from them, they cried out: 'Be now greatest among the great gods, Marduk. There is no one to equal you. From this day, your command shall not be changed, what you decree shall come to pass, your power is this—to exalt and to abase. O Marduk, our avenger, we have given you the kingship over the whole universe!'

They caused a garment to be placed in the midst of the assembly.

'Your power is now supreme. Command to destroy or to create, and your word will be fulfilled. Speak: let the garment be destroyed! Speak again: let the garment be re-made!'

Marduk spoke the word, and the garment was destroyed. Again he spoke the word, and the garment was re-made. When the gods beheld the power of his word, they all rejoiced. They did homage to him there, and cried out: 'Marduk is the King!'

They gave him the sceptre, the throne, the royal vestments and, when they had established him in all his kingly state, they said: 'Go now, Lord Marduk. Cut off the life of Tiamat, and may the North Wind bear her blood into a secret place!'

Marduk made a bow, and decreed it as his weapon; he put the first string to it, the first arrow to the string. He hung the bow beside him, and in his right hand grasped a club. Before him he set the lightning-stroke. He filled himself with flame that shone out all around him. Then Marduk made a net, in which to capture Tiamat, and he called the winds to hold its corners, so that she might not escape. The North Wind and

the South Wind, the East Wind and the West Wind, all came at
Marduk's bidding and waited on his word. Next, Marduk
created more winds to walk behind him into battle—Imhullu,
the evil wind; the Cyclone and the Hurricane; the Fourfold and
the Sevenfold Winds; the Whirlwind; the Unrivalled. Marduk
sent forth the seven winds that he had made, and they rose up,
travelling behind him, to trouble Tiamat. Marduk took up the
Rain Flood, his weapon, and drove onward in the Chariot of
Storm. It was drawn by four dread horses—Trampler, Flier,
Destructive and the fearful Pitiless. All their teeth were
poisoned fangs, and the four were schooled for battle, to tear
apart and trample down. Their hooves struck sparks of
lightning as they carried him to war. A panoply of terror flashed
on his breast; around his head there burned a ring of flames as
bright and fiery as the sun. Between his lips he grasped a
charm, and in his hand a healing plant to ward off poison. Thus
he went, with the gods all close behind.

When Marduk came to Tiamat, he looked into her heart
to read there her design; she did not flinch. He turned his
thought on Kingu; Kingu's mind became disordered, his

will-power was destroyed, he could not fight. The helpers who were marching at his side saw Marduk briefly, they saw his glory shine out and then their sight grew dark. Blinded, they, like Kingu, failed Tiamat, their mother, who sent up a roar of anger and of defiant pride.

Marduk took up the Rain Flood, and he said: 'Tiamat, you have risen in pride, and stirred up conflict. You have raised up high one of your first-born, Kingu, in the place of ancient Apsu. You have made his word greater than the word of Anu, for you placed the tablets of fate upon his breast. Evil the deed! And evil the designs that you purpose against Anshar and his sons. Step forward now, for you and I will join in single combat. We must prove which is most fit to rule, you, Tiamat, or I. If you prevail, then anarchy will reign; if I prevail, the order of the gods. This is the testing-time.'

When Tiamat heard his words, she was enraged. She grew so frenzied that she lost her senses, her wits were in disorder and no plan could take shape in her mind for conquering him. She screamed defiance and her great limbs shook, her body and her thoughts beyond control. She sang spells wildly, and she

cursed the King. To no avail—her magic was confused. The
war-gods sharpened weapons as they watched. They saw her
rush out, charging blindly. The Lord spread out his net
and drew her in, entangled in its meshes. Her jaws gaped wide
to swallow Marduk down, but he loosed in her face the evil
wind, Imhullu, which had run ever behind him. He drove
Imhullu down, deep into her belly. She swelled up, distended
by the wind, and could not close her gaping jaws. Lord
Marduk took his bow and notched an arrow to the string. He shot
it, and it sped straight down her throat into her heart. It
stuck, and quivered. Tiamat fell dead, and Marduk placed his
foot upon her neck.

Her troops turned back and tried to flee away, but they were
so surrounded by that time that there was no escaping Marduk's
wrath. He bound them, broke their weapons, cast them all
into his fishing-net. They grovelled there, trying to hide in
corners in their fear, and wept most bitterly. He cast them into
prison, where he set this burden on them, that they must always serve the younger gods, and bring them food and drink.
As for Kingu, Marduk took from him the tablets of fate and
fastened them upon his own breast. Now, indeed, his word
was supreme.

Marduk turned back now to his fallen foe. He cut her
arteries through to drain the blood, and caused the North
Wind to bear it away into a secret hiding-place. Her carcase
he split down into two parts, like a mussel. Half he set on high
and it was Heaven. Next, he measured out the Apsu, and then
spread the other half, like a canopy, above the ancient ocean
of sweet waters; this was Earth. Now there were three regions,
and Marduk gave them lords. He entrusted the Apsu to Ea, his
father, who first had made it; Heaven he then gave into the hands

of Anu; the realm between, the Earth with the air upon its face, the Esharra, went to the god Enlil. Next, Marduk made the stars and strewed them in the sky. He sent the planets wheeling round, and caused the moon to shine by night, to wax and also wane. When all this was accomplished, he turned to Ea and he said: 'Father, I will make blood and bone. I will call it "man". We will lift the yoke of service from the bowed and humbled necks of all the First-born, that they may have rest. The race of men, instead, shall feed us all with sacrifice.'

Ea said: 'You must destroy one of the First-born. Let his blood be given to make the new mankind.'

So Marduk spoke to all the gods and asked: 'Who was it who roused Tiamat to war? Who did she exalt, who had command? Let him who did this be delivered up that I may punish him.'

The gods replied: 'It was Kingu who did this. Kingu is to blame.' They led him out, and cut his arteries through. With his spilt blood the race of men was made and set on earth to multiply and spread, and in each place to bear the burden of the service of the gods. The First-born were released. Lord Marduk then divided up the whole host that he ruled, appointing half to Heaven, half to Earth. They cried out: 'Lord, who has freed us from all service and the need to find our bread, how shall we thank you? Come, let us build on Earth a sanctuary for ourselves where we may rest, and in it let us raise a throne for Marduk, Sun-god of the Gods.'

They built the temple, Esagila, with its tower, and in it raised a throne. From that time on, Lord Marduk had it for his own abode, and the gods' most favoured home was Babylon.

2. The Story of the Flood

In the Old Testament, Jehovah instructed the clan of Abraham to depart 'from Ur of the Chaldees to go into the land of Canaan' (Gen. xi : 31.). They set out in about 2300 BC, and they may have brought with them from Sumer legends and beliefs that were later adapted to fit in with the worship of Jehovah. The Hebrews were back in Babylonia during the Exile (sixth century BC), and between the entry into Canaan and the Exile, they had ample opportunity to learn the religious beliefs of the Babylonians, for tablets containing poems about Ereshkigal and Adapa have been excavated at Tel-el-Amarna in Egypt, which show that the Babylonian language and literature had reached Palestine and Egypt even before the Hebrews crossed the Jordan. Their leaders, at least, might have heard Babylonian spoken around them while in captivity in Egypt, up to the Exodus in 1250 BC, for between 1800 and 1400 BC it was the language of diplomacy used between the kings of South-west Asia and their Egyptian overlords. At whichever period in history the contact took place, it was fruitful. The many resemblances between the Hebrew and earlier Babylonian myths of the Creation and the Flood cannot be due to chance. The flood-myths in particular are so similar that they are believed to have come from the same source, a Sumerian story. There survives a fragment of a Sumerian flood-story in which the hero is called Ziusudra ('Life of long days'), and this same person appears in an official document called the Sumerian King-list as the last king of Shuruppak before the flood. This same information is also given in the Epic of Gilgamesh, *but this time the king is called Utnapishtim ('I have found life'). Ziusudra–*

Utnapishtim may have been a real king, and perhaps the legend grew up in connection with a particularly bad local flood, such as those traced by archaeologists in their excavations of Babylonian cities. Certainly enough of the Sumerian story survives to show that it must be a forerunner of the Babylonian versions, the fullest of which is contained in the Epic of Gilgamesh. *Here, the survivor tells the story in his own words and, properly enough, begins at the point when he is warned of the flood. Because of this, we do not hear the reasons for the drowning of mankind. These are given in the fragments of another Babylonian poem, the* Epic of Atramhasis, *which was written down in the year 1692* BC. *There is some evidence to suggest that the writer of this poem knew the story as found in the* Epic of Gilgamesh, *so I have assumed that the two versions would have resembled each other if both were complete, and have simply added one to the other to produce a full account.*

We saw in the introduction to Marduk and Tiamat *that many clay tablets were brought back to the British Museum and eventually deciphered there. One day, an assistant at the Museum, called George Smith, noticed what appeared to be a flood-story very like that in the Old Testament. Excitement ran high, for up to then most people believed that the Bible was literally the word of God. How could such a story have been written down before the Bible itself? Smith published the Babylonian flood-story in 1873, and the fact had to be accepted that both the Hebrews and the Babylonians shared the same myth, propably derived from an even earlier civilisation.*

It is useful to remember that in Babylonia, which had a very hot climate, there was too little rain to water the fields, so that crops depended on the annual flooding of the rivers for their growth. This is why Enlil has to stop the springs in the hills where the rivers rose, as well as the rain itself, when he wishes to produce a drought. Also bear in mind that in hot countries, houses usually have flat roofs, otherwise you will wonder how the flooded world can look as 'level as a roof'.

AFTER the gods made man, there came a time when the wide land teemed, the people multiplied and bellowed like wild oxen, till their noise smote on the ears of Enlil. Because of the tumult of mankind he could not sleep, and at last he called a meeting of the gods.

In the assembly, Enlil said to them: 'Great is the noise of mankind. I am disturbed by all their tumult and I cannot sleep. Therefore let us destroy them. Let there blow like a wind upon them sickness and disease, headache and malaria, and straightway the pestilence will silence all their noise.'

At his word there *was* malaria and the noise of mankind died, and all was quiet as the living mourned the dead. But Utna-pishtim, King of Shurrupak, turned his thoughts to Ea, his own god, and the wise man prayed: 'Lord! Hear your people groan! The whole land is laid waste by pestilence sent on us by the anger of the gods. Was it for this that you created us, to live our lives in fear? Let the pestilence be ended, Lord, I pray.'

Ea answered: 'There is evil in the land. Yet, Utnapishtim, you are dear to me, and for the love I bear you, I will try whether the gods can be appeased by prayer. So pray, and cause your people all to pray. It may be that the pestilence will end.'

Then Utnapishtim prayed; his people prayed; and Ea's pleading softened Enlil's heart. He cut off the malaria and disease, the sickness and the headache. Health returned, and mankind soon forgot the pestilence.

A time came round again when the wide land teemed, a time came round when the people multiplied and bellowed like wild oxen, till their noise smote on the ears of Enlil. Because of the tumult of mankind, he could not sleep, and at last he called a meeting of the gods.

In the assembly, Enlil said to them: 'The people are more numerous than before. I am disturbed by all their tumult and I cannot sleep. Therefore let us destroy them. Let the fields grow white with salt, dried up beneath the sun. Let the fig-tree die, the fruits of earth all fail. Let Adad of the Storm withhold his rain. Let a great wind blow and pen the clouds like sheep, so that they cannot shed their rain on earth. Let the fountains in the far hills be stopped up, so that no floods come with the spring. Let there be drought!'

The fields grew white with salt, the fig-tree died, the fruits of earth all failed, there was no rain. The fountains in the far hills were stopped up so that no floods came with the spring, and there was drought. A first, a second, and a third year passed; the people grew thin. A fourth year came and they wandered downcast through the city streets, praying for rain. When the fifth arrived, the daughter begged for food at the door of her mother; the mother would not open. But when the sixth year came, the door was opened to her; she went inside; they ate her. One house fed on the other, and the whole land lived in fear.

Then Utnapishtim, King of Shurrupak, turned his thoughts to Ea, his own lord, and the wise man prayed: 'Lord! Hear your people groan! The whole land is laid waste by this long drought, sent on us by the anger of the gods. Was it for this that you created us, to live our lives in fear? Let the great drought soon be ended, Lord, I pray.'

Ea answered: 'There is evil in the land. Yet, Utnapishtim, you are dear to me, and for the love I bear you, I will try whether the gods can be appeased by prayer. It may be that the drought will have an end.'

Then Utnapishtim prayed; his people prayed; and Ea's pleading softened Enlil's heart. The fountains were unstopped and sent down floods; the wind died down and rain began to fall; the fig-tree and the fruits of earth revived, and the parched fields drank and put forth sprouting grain. When food returned, mankind forgot the drought.

A time came round again when the wide land teemed, a time came round when the people multiplied and bellowed like wild oxen, till their noise smote on the ears of Enlil. Because of the tumult of mankind he could not sleep, and at last he called a meeting of the gods.

In the assembly, Enlil said to them: 'The people are more numerous than before. I am disturbed by all their tumult and I cannot sleep. Therefore let us destroy them, every one. Let Adad thunder in the black storm-cloud, and Ninurta trample the dikes and river-banks. Let the wind blow and let the tempest rage. Let flood overwhelm the land and drown mankind.'

At Enlil's words, Ishtar the Queen of Heaven cried out and bewailed her people. Ea said: 'How can you do this, Enlil? The flood that you command will drown all of the men that we have made. Was it for this we made them? Was it not to bring us food, to offer sacrifice? And when all are drowned, how shall we fare?'

But Enlil would not listen to his words, would not heed Ea's pleading. The wise god, the Lord of the Sweet Waters, then resolved to save his favourite, Utnapishtim, from the flood.

That way he thought to keep mankind alive for the service of the gods in after-times.

A dream of storm came to the pious king, a dream of tempest, hurricane, and flood. He woke in fear and started from his bed. He hurried to the temple of his lord, and cried out: 'Ea! Ea! I have dreamed a dream of flood and tempest. Make its meaning known. Make it known, that I may guard the land.'

Ea said: 'I cannot tell to *you* the secrets of the gods, betray their counsels to a mortal. Yet I must save you if I can, so listen well at the reed-wall of your house. There is no law that says I may not whisper to the reeds.'

Then Utnapishtim listened by the wall, and presently he heard a voice begin: 'Listen, reed-house! Wall, hear Ea's words! Tell Utnapishtim all that I have said: "The Gods of Heaven plan to send a flood to silence all the people. Leave your house, abandon your possessions, save your life. You must build a ship of equal width and length, and cause the seed of every living thing to go inside it."'

Utnapishtim heard. He said: 'I will obey. But what shall I tell my people, who will ask where I am going?'

'You must tell them, "Enlil hates me, so I must leave his city and go down to dwell with Ea in the Apsu." Tell them this and they will question you no more, but be content.'

Then Utnapishtim said: 'I have not built even the smallest boat until this day. So draw me out a plan upon the ground, that I may build it to your own design.'

Ea drew a plan upon the ground. As soon as the first light of morning came, Utnapishtim called his craftsmen out to see the plan and start work on the ship. They collected what was needed in four days—ropes and timbers, asphalt, pitch and oil. On the fifth day, Utnapishtim planned the frame. One hundred and twenty cubits was its length, its width and also depth. Its upper deck measured an acre. Inside were built six more, so that the ship had seven storeys, each of these divided in nine sections. It was caulked, and when the whole was ready, then the king gathered up his goods and precious things, and loaded them on board. Next he sent his family inside, his relatives and craftsmen. Last of all, he caused the birds and beasts to enter in. Shamash the sun-god set a time for him: 'When the rain begins at evening, close the ship.'

The evening came. The rain began to fall. The king went in the ark and closed the door. He gave his boatman charge over the ship, and waited for the flood.

As soon as the first light of morning came, a black cloud rose swiftly from the sky's far rim, and in it thundered Adad, Lord of Storm. Ninurta trampled down the river-banks and caused the dikes to crumble. Darkness fell, seared by the dreadful lightning which flamed out when the Annunaki, Judges of the Dead, raised high their torches, prowling through the land. That first day, like a battle raged the storm. It was so dark no man could see the next, and none on earth be recognised from

Heaven. Terror seized the great gods, and they fled, fearful of the waters, ever higher, up to the Heaven of Anu, sore afraid. They cowered there like dogs. Ishtar cried out: 'How could I let such war loose on the land? How could I let such evil counsel pass in the assembly of the gods, and say no word! Like the spawn of fish my people fill the sea!'

The gods wept with her. Six days and six nights the tempest raged, and the flood rose up and up. But when the seventh day came, the storm died down, the rain stopped falling and the boiling flood, which had battled like an army, ceased to rise. The sea grew quiet, and a great calm fell.

Utnapishtim opened a window. Light streamed in and fell upon his face. The sun's bright rays lit up the darkest corners of the ark. Utnapishtim looked out on the sea. Everything was still. There was no noise. Mankind had turned to clay beneath the waves. The king sat down and wept; the tears ran down, as Utnapishtim wept for lost mankind.

At length, he rose and, looking from the ship, scanned every quarter for some sight of land, for some sign of the boundaries of the sea. But there were none. The water stretched all round,

and all the world was level as a roof. But when the ark had
sailed for one more day, a mountain-peak emerged, a little
stretch not covered by the water. When the ship landed on
Mount Nisir, it held fast. For six days it held fast and did
not float. Utnapishtim knew the rain was over and gone. On
the seventh day, the king took up a dove and let her go. There
was no resting-place for her and she returned. He took a swallow
next and let her go. There was no resting-place for her and she
returned. He took a raven last and let her go. She went away
and when the raven saw that the waters had abated, she
flew round, she fed, she cawed, and she did not return. Then
Utnapishtim set free all the birds to fly about the land. Upon the
peak he held a sacrifice and heaped up sacred fires with
cedar-wood and myrtle. When the gods smelled the sweet
savour of the sacrifice, they gathered round like flies.

As soon as Ishtar came, she touched her beads of lapis lazuli
and she said: 'As surely as I shall not forget the necklace which
I wear, so also shall I remember the days of wrath and not
forget! Let the gods share in the offering—all save he who
caused the deluge, he who drowned mankind.'

c   33

But Enlil came, and when he saw the ship, he shouted out in fury: 'Who did this? Which one of you has tricked me? You all knew no man was meant to live through my great flood!'

Ninurta answered: 'Ea has done this. Enlil, was it wisdom to act against his counsel, when none but he foresees the ends of all our actions?'

Ea said: 'Enlil, listen. How could you loose this flood upon them? Rein mankind in, lest they become too wild, but do not pull so tight that their breath fails! Instead of the great flood, why not a lion? Instead of the great flood, why not a drought? Instead of the great flood, why not disease, to diminish mankind but not destroy all men? Punish them with these in days to come. And as for Utnapishtim, he is wise, and learned your secret counsel in a dream. What shall we do for him?'

Enlil's heart was moved by Ea's words. He repented of his wrath against mankind. He took the hands of Utnapishtim and his wife and led them up into the ship. When they came on board again, he stood between them as they knelt down on the deck. He touched their foreheads and he blessed them. Enlil said: 'From this day on, you two shall be as gods and you shall live for ever where the sun, even the bright Lord Shamash, rises up at morning in far Dilmun. You alone, of all mankind, shall have the precious gift of everlasting life, and you shall walk for ever in the Garden of the Gods.'

3. Gilgamesh

When Smith published the Babylonian flood-story, he issued with it a summary of the poem in which it was embedded. This poem was the Epic of Gilgamesh, and it amazed people to think that this epic was at least one and a half thousand years older than Homer's Iliad, the oldest poem they then knew of.

Gilgamesh may have been a real man, for he appears in the Sumerian King-list as the fifth king in Uruk. He is accredited with a semi-divine origin, for his mother was Ninsun, a minor goddess of Uruk, and his father, according to the King-list, was 'the high priest of Kullab', a district within the same city. Gilgamesh was clearly regarded as superhuman by the writer of the Epic, who gives his height as eleven cubits, or approximately eighteen feet, and the weight of his armour as ten talents, or forty-two stones. The King-list itself says that he reigned for a hundred and twenty-six years, so he was clearly more than man!

Whether real or legendary, he was famous throughout the Near East from about 2000 BC down to the seventh century BC when the fullest version of the Epic was written. This was at the command of Ashurbanipal, whom we mentioned before. Among the texts that his servants brought back to Nineveh were poems about Gilgamesh. There are several stories about him written in Sumerian and dating from the first centuries following 2000 BC. The Babylonians may have woven such stories together into one epic already, but our only full version, the present Epic of Gilgamesh, was 'written down and collated in the palace of Ashurbanipal, King of the World, King of Assyria'.

The whole of the Assyrian version was not found at once.

Other tablets containing parts of this version have been found at different times and the Epic *pieced together more fully. Some gaps in the text have been filled by readings taken from versions written in the languages of other Near Eastern peoples, but there are still bits missing, and some mysteries remain. What was the spell laid on the Forest Gate, and just what were the Images of Stone?*

The story told to Gilgamesh by Utnapishtim is in the main the Story of the Flood *which precedes this. Although the story of the Flood is related as part of the Assyrian version of the* Epic, *it was probably not part of the early Gilgamesh-cycle but a self-contained and independent myth.*

The Bull of Heaven, is a personification of drought, hence Anu's anxiety as to the provisions that Ishtar has made for feeding men and cattle.

The roller is a bird, so named because it loops and rolls in flight during the breeding season. Its cry resembled the Babylonian word kappi *meaning 'my wing'. The cry and the peculiar flight probably gave rise to the legend of the broken wing.*

LISTEN to the tale of Gilgamesh, of Gilgamesh the golden, King of Kings, who carved his name where great men's names were carved; and where no names were, there he built an altar to the gods.

He was the King in Uruk, where he raised great walls and ramparts, and the temple of Eanna for the father of the gods, Anu, Lord of all the Firmament, and for Ishtar, Queen of War and Love. There was no city on the face of earth more splendid than Uruk; there was no king more brave and strong than Gilgamesh, its lord. But he was two parts god and one

part man, his human form unable to contain the restless vigour of divinity. So he became a tyrant and he took the young men of the city from their homes to labour on the temples and the walls, performing tasks that were beyond their strength. Sons lost fathers, fathers lost their sons—but worse than this in all the people's eyes was that he forced young maidens and new brides to be his own wives, leaving those they loved and those who loved them stricken with despair. The old men grumbled in their houses every day:

'Such is the shepherd of his flock, such is our king! No ravening wolf that slaughters the young lambs is crueller than he is, for he leaves no son to his old father and no bride to her new-wedded husband. Is there none who can restrain this tyrant, and relieve the sorrow that is weighing on our hearts, through the fault of Gilgamesh the King?'

The Making of Enkidu

The gods heard lamentations rising up out of the city, and they went before the throne of Anu, god of Uruk.

'Lord,' they said, 'in Uruk sons lose fathers, fathers sons, husbands lose wives upon their marriage-day, all through the fault of Gilgamesh the King.'

The goddess of creation, Aruru, was standing by, and they all turned on her: '*You* made him, Aruru, now you must make a match for him, his equal, strength for strength. Let them strive together, wild heart with wild heart, and in their striving let the city rest.'

The goddess formed an image in her mind. She washed her hands and, pinching off some clay, she shaped it to the pattern she had made and cast it on the plains, where it became a man like none those lands had ever seen. His name was Enkidu. He had Ninurta's strength, but his hair hung down his back as thick as grain, and long as any woman's. He was huge, and had a shaggy hide like Samuqan the cattle god. He roamed the plains and drank at water-holes with wild gazelle, neither he nor they knowing that he was of human-kind.

But a trapper met him one day, face to face, down at a water-hole; a second day, and then a third they met. The trapper's face was frozen with cold fear. He took his game and went home to his house. His fear locked up his heart; he could not speak, but seeing him look strange, his father said: 'What has befallen you, my son?'

'Father,' said the trapper, 'a wild man roams the plains and drinks at water-holes with the gazelle. He eats grass like the beasts and sucks their milk. He sets them free from all my traps, fills in the pits. I am afraid to hunt. What shall I do?'

His father said: 'Go now to Gilgamesh, the King in Uruk, and tell *him* your tale. Then he will send a temple-woman here, for if she sits at evening by the wells the wild man, seeing her, will draw to her, attracted by her beauty; he will know that he

is one of her kind. Then the beasts will run from him, as from all other men, and he will leave the plains.'

The trapper went, and told the King his tale.

'Lord,' said the trapper, 'a wild man roams the plains and drinks at water-holes with the gazelle. He eats grass like the beasts and sucks their milk. He sets them free from all my traps, fills in the pits. I am afraid to hunt. What shall I do?'

'Take back a temple-woman to the plains, for if she sits at evening at the wells the wild man, seeing her, will draw to her, attracted by her beauty; he will know that he is one of her kind. Then the beasts will run from him, as from all other men, and he will leave the plains.'

The trapper took a temple-woman back. They journeyed to the wells and there sat down to wait for Enkidu. He did not come the first day, nor the next, but on the third he came with the gazelle down from the plains, at evening, at the setting of the sun. When he saw the temple-woman, she seemed fairer than the beasts; when she spoke, her voice seemed sweeter than the birds'. The wild man stayed for six days by the wells and from the woman learned the speech of men, but when he would have gone back to his herd, the wild beasts ran from him, as they would run from any man. He grieved and was perplexed, for now he could not run as fast as they. He went back to the wells and there sat down at the woman's feet, to learn what he must do.

In Uruk, Gilgamesh awoke from sleep and, rising, went to seek his mother out in her temple. When he came there, he bowed down and said: 'My mother, I have dreamed a dream. A star fell out of heaven at my feet. I tried to lift it but I was too weak. I tried to move it but could not prevail. All the land had gathered round the star, the men thronged round it and some kissed its feet. I put my forehead to it, raised it up. I lifted it and carried it to you, and you put it on a par with me, your son.'

Ninsun, the wise one, answered Gilgamesh: 'The star of heaven which fell down at your feet, which I myself put on a par with you, is the wild man of the plains and like a star is his great strength. He is the friend who, wild heart for wild heart, will equal you and be your second self, to guard your back in battle and in peace sit by your side; to laugh when you laugh and to share your grief. He will not forsake you.'

That same night, Gilgamesh dreamed again and, waking, went to Ninsun in her temple.

'Mother, I have dreamed another dream. In Uruk lay an axe, and the people thronged about it in the street. I laid it at your feet and you yourself put it on a par with me, your son.'

Ninsun, the wise one, answered Gilgamesh: 'The axe you saw is the wild man of the plains. His strength is like an axe. He is the friend who, wild heart for wild heart, will equal you and be your second self, to guard your back in battle and in peace sit by our side; to laugh when you laugh and to share your grief. He will not forsake you.'

'May I be granted such a friend,' said Gilgamesh.

Meanwhile, the woman talked to Enkidu.

'*You* are no beast to crop the grass,' she said, 'or drink at water-holes with the gazelle. You are no wild man now. Come, Enkidu, come with me into Uruk, where the king is Gilgamesh the Tyrant, whose vast strength is such that nowhere can he find his match. Now, therefore, he prevails over his people like some great wild ox, not caring for their pain.'

Enkidu grew eager at her words. He longed to find a friend— could this be he? Could this be one to share his secret thoughts?

He told the woman: 'Take me to Uruk, where Gilgamesh walks restless in his strength. I will challenge him and cry: "I am the one born on the plains, the strongest of all men, come here to change the proud ways of the tyrant Gilgamesh!"'

'You have no cause to boast,' the woman said, 'for though you may be strongest of all *men*, yet he is two parts god, and stronger still. Never does he rest by night or day. But I will show you him, if you will come to Uruk, where each day is holiday and people walk the streets in gay attire, as bright as butterflies; where all the air is filled with scents of spices and perfumes; where wines abound to make your heart rejoice; where all would be as joyous as the sun, if Gilgamesh the King would mend his ways.'

The woman halved her robe and clothed the man. She led him, like a mother, by the hand down to the sheep-folds, where the shepherds were. They gathered round to see him, brought him bread; he stared at it, because he did not know how he was to eat it. They brought wine, but he was used to drink milk from the beasts and when he tried to lap like any dog, the shepherds laughed and made a mock of him. When they had taught him both to eat and drink, he rubbed his hairy body down with oil and then put on a garment. Now, indeed, he seemed to them the comeliest of men. He was the shepherds' watchman; since he had come they slept at night, while he caught the wolves and lions that fell upon their flocks.

But one day, by the sheep-folds where he sat, he lifted up his eyes and saw a man come running from the city, and he said: 'Woman, go bring him to me. Ask him why he comes here.'

She called out: 'Why do you come here?'

'For help,' the man replied. 'There is to be a wedding at the meeting-house, and Gilgamesh will surely come and carry off the bride to be his wife. Will you not stop him, Enkidu?'

The wild man shook, his face went white with anger at the stranger's words. He set out with the woman and they hastened to Uruk. They entered into the city and, when they reached the market-place, the people gathered round. Some said: 'He looks like Gilgamesh!'

'No, he is much shorter, though heavier of bone, I think.'

'They *say* he roamed the plains and ate the grass like any beast!'

The people made him welcome: 'A mighty man has come to us. He has arisen like a god to be a match for Gilgamesh!'

And when the King came through the town to the meeting-house of Uruk, his way was barred by Enkidu, who stood there in the street and would not move aside for him. He blocked the doorway with his foot to prevent the King from going in. The two began to fight. They grappled with each other, both snorting like two mighty bulls. They broke the doorpost, and the wall was shaken by their blows. They wrestled in the doorway,

43

in the street, and in the market-place, till Gilgamesh, because he was part-god, threw Enkidu. He threw him to the ground and, standing there, he looked at him. Then his anger was abated and he turned to go away. After he had turned, the fallen Enkidu called out to him: 'Your mother, Ninsun, bore a son exalted over all! Enlil himself decreed for you your kingship over Uruk. There is none like you, for your strength is more than that of man.'

'It is a god's,' said Gilgamesh. 'I could not so have thrown you had it been otherwise, and yet I found it hard to do. Truly, you are my equal! Will you be my companion, the friend to know my secret thoughts?'

'I will,' said Enkidu, and they sealed a pact of friendship which would endure between them in happiness and sorrow, while both their lives should last.

The Slaying of Humbaba

Gilgamesh sat in Uruk and was sad, pondering the life of men, and death. He fell asleep at last and dreamed a dream of his own dying, because he was one third a mortal man and shared their bitter fate. He woke to sorrow, and he told his dream to Enkidu, his dear friend.

'Do not grieve,' said Enkidu. 'You will not live for ever, yet still yours is the kingship, yours the power to rule. Deal justly by your people, win their love, and leave behind you an everlasting name.'

'My name will not endure without brave deeds,' said Gilgamesh, 'and therefore let us go into the Cedar Forest to win fame.'

Enkidu sighed bitterly.

'Why set your heart on this?'

'In that forest dwells Humbaba, the great giant, set there by Enlil to safeguard the trees, but he has grown too proud. So let us go and fell him, cut him down, uproot the evil that is in that land.'

'When I was as a beast and roamed the plains, I saw that land. The Cedar Forest runs a full ten thousand leagues from side to side, and if some creature stirs within its depths, Humbaba hears though sixty leagues away. What man would venture into his dark realm, would choose to meet the keeper of the trees, whose breath is hot as fire, whose mighty roar is like the fearful thunder of the storm? No man on earth can equal *him* in strength, for Enlil made him perilous to men. Weakness takes hold of those who enter in his dark dominions. We shall not return.'

'What man can live for ever, Enkidu? Our days are numbered and our time runs fast, and all our deeds are but a breath of wind. Already, in the city, you fear death—what has become of all your manly strength? I will walk before you. You may call: "Gilgamesh, go on! Be not afraid!" from where you stand in safety. If I fall, my name will live for ever. They will say: "Gilgamesh has fallen in fight with the terrible Humbaba", and sons as yet unborn will speak my name with pride in days to come. Your fearfulness afflicts my heart with grief, but I shall still go on, still put my hand to this great task and cut the cedar down. I shall give orders to my armourers; they will forge for us weapons fit for gods, so come with me.'

Gilgamesh set his armourers to work. Great swords they cast, and made them sheaths of gold; forged monstrous axes for a giant's bane. When all was ready, each of them would arm with massive weapons of ten talents' weight.

Gilgamesh called the elders of Uruk and said: 'O elders, listen to your King. I wish to see him of whom all men talk, him with whose dread name the lands are filled. In the Cedar Forest I will vanquish him and cause the lands to hear of Gilgamesh.'

The elders of Uruk said to their King: 'You are young, O Gilgamesh. Your heart is rash. You do not know what you propose to do. Humbaba is no man like other men! Who is there that can stand against his might? His roar is like the storm, his mouth holds fire, and he breathes out death to all mankind. Why must you do this thing? For you must fail.'

Gilgamesh looked at Enkidu, and laughed.

'What shall I tell them? That I am afraid? Would you have us sit here all our days, each growing old in fear and idleness?'

The elders said: 'If you must go, then may your patron god protect you; may he bring you safely home; to the quay of Uruk cause you to return.'

Gilgamesh bowed himself down to the ground before the sun-god, Shamash, and he prayed: 'I go, O Shamash, and I

raise my hands to you in prayer. Let it be well with me. Bring me back to Uruk. Keep me safe.'

Gilgamesh called his friend to go with him and in the temple have the omens read. He came out weeping, tears ran down his face, for the omens spelled disaster.

'Must I walk alone, down a road which I have never gone before without your guidance, Shamash?' cried the King.

His workmen brought the weapons, the massive swords and axes, and placed a bow of Anshan in his hand. The elders gave their blessing once again, and for the journey counselled Gilgamesh.

'Do not trust in your strength! Let Enkidu go on before you. He has seen the way, has walked the road that leads up to the Gate. He who goes before will save his friend. May Shamash grant you victory. May he cause your eyes to see the fulfilment of the vows that you have made. May he open up closed paths, and send propitious dreams, and cause you to slay Humbaba like a child. In the river of the forest, wash your feet. Every evening dig a well and let there be pure water always in your water-skin for an offering to Shamash.'

Enkidu said: 'Come, friend. Let us set out on our way. Let your heart be not afraid, but follow me.'

Gilgamesh said: 'First, we must take farewell of Ninsun, my wise mother. Let us go into the temple Egalmah, her home.'

The friends went hand in hand to Egalmah, the palace of the goddess.

'Hear me, Mother,' said King Gilgamesh, 'for I must tread a strange road from today, and from today face dangers unforeseen, until the day when I return again. I must slay the keeper of the trees to win myself an everlasting name, so pray for me to Shamash that I may uproot the evil that is in his land.'

Ninsun the Queen put on her finest robes, and on her head the royal diadem. She mounted to the roof of Egalmah, where stood the Sun Lord's altar, nearest Heaven, and throwing incense on the sacred fire, she sent her prayers up with the winding smoke.

'Why did you give my son a restless heart? Now that you have touched him and he walks a strange road, facing dangers unforeseen, guard him until the day that he returns. When you have turned your eye away from earth, entrust him to the Watchmen of the Night till you come back with Aya, Bride of Dawn, and your bright glances watch the world again.'

Ninsun put out the incense and went down to where her son still stood with Enkidu.

'Enkidu,' she said, 'from this day on, you are my child. I have adopted you. Here is my amulet; it is a pledge that I have taken you to be my son. Into your keeping I give Gilgamesh, your brother; keep him safe, and bring him back to me when all is done.'

The friends bade her farewell. They set out now, and as they left the gates, the elders cried: 'In our assembly we have paid heed to your words; pay heed to ours in turn, O Gilgamesh! Let Enkidu protect the friend he loves.'

'Fear not,' said Enkidu. 'All will be well.'

For twenty leagues they walked before they ate; and thirty more before they stopped for sleep. A journey of six weeks was made by them in just three days, and after they had crossed the seventh mountain in their path, they saw ahead the Gate into the Forest. It was shut, and guarded by a watchman, set there by Humbaba, the great giant; less in size, but as terrible of aspect as it seemed the giant could be, and Gilgamesh fell back.

'Remember the vows you made!' cried Enkidu. 'Stand forth and slay this watchman!'

At his words, the King took heart and said: 'We must be quick. He is used to put on seven coats of mail when he goes into battle. One is on. If we delay, he will be fully armed, and how then shall we take his life from him?'

Like a furious wild ox, the watchman roared, and cried out:

'Go! You may not enter in! This is the Cedar Forest, and the realm of Humbaba the giant. Mortal men may not pass by these gates.'

'Yet we shall pass,' said Gilgamesh the King.

The two advanced and struck the watchman down. As yet he had put on but one mail coat, and so his life was taken, though he was the servant of the giant, great of strength and towering of stature. Enkidu stepped forward to the Gate, when once its keeper lay dead on the ground. Such was its beauty and its craftsmanship that he could not bear to strike it with his axe, but pushed it open with his outstretched hand.

He sprang back with a cry, for on the Gate lay deep enchantments.

Enkidu cried out: 'O let us not go down into the Forest; see my hand! When I touched the Gate, my hand lost all its strength and now it hangs down lifeless at my side. Some deep enchantment lies about this Gate. Let us not pass inside!'

'Should we turn back, now we have come so far?' asked Gilgamesh. 'Would you remain behind? No, stay with me. The weakness will soon pass. Together we will go into the depths of this great Forest and perform the task for which we came. Forget your thoughts of death.'

They passed inside the Gate and caught their breath. Their words were stilled to silence. They were still, and gazed upon the Forest, the green mountain. They beheld the height of the cedars and the broad path through the trees where the giant was used to walk in the cool and pleasant shade. Greener were the shadows of the Mountain of the Cedar than of any other place, and Gilgamesh the King dug a well at sunset there, to offer up to Shamash waters from the earth. He poured out meal and prayed: 'Mountain of the Cedar, send me a dream to show me if my fate be good or bad.'

The two lay down to sleep. When midnight came, Gilgamesh awoke and roused his friend: 'Enkidu, I dreamed that we two stood within deep gorges, when a mountain fell and by its side we seemed as small as flies. I dreamed again; again the mountain fell. It struck me down; the mountain caught my foot. Then light blazed out and in it was a form more beautiful than any in the land. He took the mountain off me, pulled me out, and giving me water, set me on my feet.'

Enkidu said: 'This dream was fortunate. The mountain was Humbaba. It must mean that we shall likewise bring about his fall, and by the help of Shamash, Lord of Light.'

They travelled on next day, and once again Gilgamesh, at evening, dug a well in honour of the Sun God, and again he scattered meal upon the ground. This time he prayed: 'Mountain, bring a dream for Enkidu, to show him if his fate be good or bad.'

The Mountain sent a dream to Enkidu. He thought that in his dream a cold rain fell, but he kept silent, for he was afraid. Then Gilgamesh awoke. He said: 'My friend, did you not call me? Did you not touch me, or has some god now passed this way? I have dreamed a third dream. In it lightning filled the air. Heaven thundered, earth resounded, daylight failed and darkness fell. The brightness vanished and the fire went out. Then death rained down and turned the world to ashes and to dust.'

'My friend, be not afraid,' said Enkidu. 'For this dream too, may mean that we shall slay Humbaba, and his fall will be as dreadful as the storms that you have seen.'

Though he spoke cheerful words, his heart was cold. The two resolved to go on with their task. Gilgamesh took an axe up in his hand and he cut down a cedar. Far away, the giant

Humbaba heard the noise. He grew enraged: 'Who has come among my trees? Who is cutting down my cedar?'

Then from Heaven the Sun God Shamash called: 'Be not afraid! Go forward without fear—you have my help.'

The two advanced. With great strides from his house the giant Humbaba came and horror fell upon the two friends' hearts, for he was huger than the tales had made him and more terrible. He fastened on the King the eye of death. The strength of Gilgamesh began to fail and, with his one sound hand, Enkidu his friend could not hope to defend him. Gilgamesh the the King called out to heavenly Shamash: 'Help me, Lord! I have honoured you! I have pursued the road decreed by fate which brought me to this place, here to cut down Humbaba, who is evil in your sight, to root out all the evil in your land.'

The Sun God heard, and called from their far caves the Great Wind, and the Whirlwind, the Tempest and the Storm, the North, the South, the Freezing Wind, the Burning Wind—all eight rose up against Humbaba and beat against his evil eyes. He was unable to go forward, unable to turn back. He was helpless, and he pleaded: 'Let me go, O Gilgamesh. You shall be my master if you spare me, I your slave. I will cut down the cedars which I have tended on the Mountain, and build a palace for you. Have mercy, Gilgamesh!'

The King was moved by his strong pleas. He said: 'Is it not right for us to set the prisoner free, for us to send the captive back to his mother's house, and to return the caught bird to his nest?'

'It is not right to set *this* prisoner free, to send *this* captive back to his mother's house, and to return *this* caught bird to his nest, if you would see *your* mother once again. Where is your judgment? What use is your strength if wisdom does not guide it? If we do not slay him, then he will turn on us. Do not listen to his pleading. He is evil and must die.'

'It will be as in the dream,' said Gilgamesh, 'the brightness of our fame will be eclipsed and all our deeds as ash, if we kill him.'

'It is not so. Our fame will be as great. The giant must die or us, and you must choose.'

Gilgamesh struck first; next Enkidu; and at the third blow Humbaba lay still.

But he was the keeper of the cedar trees, whose power made forests tremble; now his death caused the whole world to shudder, mountains move, and hills and valleys be put from their place. Yet Gilgamesh still cut the cedars down and Enkidu hacked out the twining roots as far as the Euphrates. Then they turned their faces from the Forest and went home.

The Bull of Heaven

Time passed on in peace and quietness till one day Ishtar,

cruel Queen of Love, looked from Eanna to where King Gilgamesh sat on his royal throne in robes of state. She looked and loved.

'O Gilgamesh', she said, 'if you would be my husband, I would harness to the storm a chariot of lapis lazuli and gold; on golden wheels would you ride earth and air, and all the kings and princes of the world would bow themselves before you, and give praise.'

'How could I take the Queen of Heaven for wife? Would you wear earthly garments, eat our bread? And, Lady, all men know that you break faith. For Tammuz, your young husband, women wail at the ending of the year: who let him die? You loved the roller once—and broke his wing; now he stands crying "*kappi*" in the groves. What happened to the shepherd of the herd who daily heaped up sacrifice to you? You cursed him and you turned him into a wolf. His herd boys chase him off and his own dogs tear at his flanks. Then there was Ishullanu—what of him? You offered him your love, but he refused, so in your injured pride you struck him down, and turned your father's gardener to a mole. If I became your

54

husband, you would soon grow tired of me and treat me like to them.'

A great wrath fell on Ishtar. She ascended into Heaven. She stood raging before Anu, her father, and she said: 'Gilgamesh has cursed me, and taunted me with all my deeds. He has *refused* to be my husband!'

'And if he has?' Lord Anu said. 'Have you not deserved his taunts?'

'I will have vengeance! Father—make me the Bull of Heaven, that Gilgamesh may be destroyed! If you will not do this, I will break down the Door of the Underworld and cause the dead to rise again, and they will be more numerous than the living upon earth.'

'If I do this,' said Anu, 'there will be drought for seven years. Have you fodder for the cattle and grain to feed mankind?'

'There is enough,' said Ishtar.

'Be it so, then,' Anu said.

The Bull of Heaven descended and an army marched against it. Its first snort killed six hundred men; its second snort killed more; at its third snort it saw Enkidu and charged, but he was ready. He seized it by the horns and cried out: 'Gilgamesh, be quick! Run your sword between its nape and horns.'

The Bull foamed at the mouth and tore the ground up in its rage, but Enkidu held fast and swiftly Gilgamesh thrust in his sword. The Bull fell dead. The brothers cut the heart out of the beast and offered it to Shamash, the bright sun, then took their rest.

But from the walls of Uruk went up the cry of Ishtar: 'Accursed be he who killed the Bull! Let Gilgamesh beware, for twice now he has scorned me!'

Enkidu turned toward her, tore off the right thigh of the Bull and cast it in her face: 'Thus would I do with you if only I were able to catch hold of you,' he shouted.

Ishtar sent up a wail. She called her temple-women and they set up lamentations over the right thigh of the Bull. Beside the monstrous corpse stood the King with all his craftsmen. They cut off the huge horns and hung them on the palace wall. Then the brothers washed their hands in the waters of Euphrates and rode in triumph through the streets where crowds had gathered thick, hoping to see the heroes.

The King cried out to them: 'Who is greatest?'

'The greatest of men is Gilgamesh, and next is Enkidu!'

But Enkidu was troubled in his dreams that night and, when day came, he went and told all he had dreamt to Gilgamesh the King.

'My friend, hear what a dream I had last night, when I saw Heaven. All the gods were there in council and I heard Lord Anu say: "The brothers have offended twice. First they killed Humbaba, and then the Bull of Heaven so one of them must die."

'Enlil said: "Not Gilgamesh; he is the King. Take Enkidu."

56

'Shamash answered: "He is innocent. Why, therefore, should he die? It was at *my* command these two cut down the giant Humbaba, for although he was *your* servant, the cedar-land is *mine*."

'Enlil raged at heavenly Shamash: "You go down there to earth each day and grow more man than god! They share the guilt, but Gilgamesh is King, set over Uruk by my own decree. And he is two parts god. Therefore you shall not take him. Take the one who is no more than man." '

When Enkidu had told this dream, a fever came and daily spread outward from the cankered hand that had touched the Forest Gate. Gilgamesh sat over him and grieved: 'Why do the gods take you instead of me? Though I sit and wait outside the doors of death, yet you and I will never meet again.'

Enkidu burned with fever and he cursed the Forest Gate: 'I saw you from afar, and I marvelled at your beauty, for you were made in Nippur by skilled craftsmen and your size was so exceeding great that there could not be another like you anywhere. And so I would not hurt you. O Gate, had I but known that by your beauty you would cause my death, I would not thus have spared you, would not have touched your timbers with my bare hand, but instead I would have raised my axe and hewed you down.'

Then he cursed the temple-woman, for it was she who first had brought him into Uruk and to Gilgamesh: 'May she be cast out! Let her be driven from the temple, let her haunt the shadow of the wall, let the streets become her dwelling-place. Let each hand strike her cheek!'

When Shamash heard these words, he called from Heaven: 'Why do you curse the woman? It was she who clothed your body with her garments, taught you speech, how to eat bread, and drink wine from a cup. It was she who gave you Gilgamesh the King, to be your friend and your own brother. And from him you received the high seat in his palace, the seat at his left side, so that the princes of the earth should kiss your feet. Over you the King will cause Uruk to wail; over you, when you are buried, he will mourn. He will let his hair grow long, put on a lion-skin, and wander in the desert for your sake.'

Enkidu's anger left him when he heard the words of Shamash. He lifted off the curse and gave a blessing in its place. He lay there growing weaker, with the fever burning in him and his dreams became more terrible with every night that passed.

One night, he woke and called out to his friend: 'Gilgamesh, last night the heavens groaned and the earth rang echoing with the sound. I stood alone before some dreadful thing whose face was dark as any bird of storm; who seized me in strong talons, held me fast, and choked my life out with his eagle-claw. And then he turned my arms to feathered wings and led me down that path which none walks twice, to the house of Ereshkigal, Queen of Death, to the house which the man who enters never leaves. The people there are clothed with wings like birds. They sit in darkness for eternity. Their food is dust and clay their sustenance. And there I saw the princes of the earth, their splendour brought to ashes and to dust. The Queen of Darkness sat upon her throne and, before her, squatting at her feet, was Belit-sheri, she who is the Scribe and keeps the register of all the dead. She was reading from a tablet which she held, but raised her head and saw me. She got up and stretching out her hand, took me away. And at that, I awoke. I am afraid.'

Gilgamesh said: 'Dear friend, your dream has shown that darkness is the end of mortal life.'

Enkidu's pain increased from day to day, and on the twelfth he called to Gilgamesh: 'Because of Ishtar's wrath I lie here now upon a bed of shame, not like a man who falls in battle and is blessed. But as for me, I die dishonoured.' And he spoke no more.

As soon as the first light of morning came, Gilgamesh cried: 'Elders of Uruk! It is for Enkidu my friend that I now weep. It is for Enkidu that I shed bitter tears. He was my axe, the bow in my right hand, the shield that was before me, and my joy. An evil foe has robbed me of my friend, my younger brother, who once ran with the wild ass and the panther of the plain. We two ascended mountains, we killed the Bull of Heaven, and we slew Humbaba, the keeper of the trees. O, Enkidu, where are you? Are you lost out in the darkness? What sleep has taken hold of you? Can you not hear my voice?'

Gilgamesh touched the heart of Enkidu. It did not beat.

The King then veiled his brother like a bride. Back and forth he paced before his friend and like a lion lifted up his voice, or a lioness robbed of her young cubs. He tore his hair, cast off his royal robes and wept: 'I gave to you the seat at my left side, so that the princes of the earth should kiss your feet. Now I will cause the people of Uruk to weep and wail for you, and over you, when you are buried, I will mourn. I will let my hair grow long, put on a lion-skin, and wander in the desert for your sake.'

For seven days and seven nights he wept, before he gave his brother to the earth. And then he left Uruk, and went away to wander in the wilderness in grief.

The Search for Everlasting Life

Gilgamesh wept bitterly for Enkidu his friend, and roamed the desert waste.

'Where is there any rest for me,' he cried, 'now Enkidu is dead, for black despair gnaws at my heart. As he is, I shall be. I am afraid, and therefore I will go to seek out Utnapishtim, the one man whom the gods saved from the flood that drowned the world. For him, whom men call Faraway, they set in Dilmun, in the Garden of the Gods, and gave him the gift of everlasting life. He will tell me how to win it for myself.'

He set out on his journey, wandering far till he reached the mountain Mashu which stands guard over the rising and the setting of the sun. Its peaks stretched up to Heaven, but its roots pierced down into the gloomy Underworld. The Scorpion-people kept watch at its gate; ringed with flame, their gaze was death to men. But Gilgamesh, his face dark with dismay, covered his eyes but for a moment's space against their fiery aureoles, then advanced. He gathered up his courage and bowed low.

'This a god who comes on unafraid,' said the Scorpion-man, but his wife answered him: 'He is but two parts god and one part man.'

The Scorpion-man called out to Gilgamesh. He asked: 'Why have you come here, come so far, out here to Mashu on the rim of earth?'

Gilgamesh said: 'I had a friend who died. Because of him, I travelled to this place. My life is empty now that he is dead and as he is, so one day shall I be. I shall lie down and never rise again. So I seek Utnapishtim, for they say that he alone has everlasting life; he will tell me how to win it for myself.'

'No living man before you has dared go into the mountain Mashu, for inside there stretch twelve leagues of darkness without light, from the rising to the setting of the sun.'

'Yet I must go,' said Gilgamesh. 'In sorrow or in pain, in sighing or in weeping, I must go.'

'The gate is open for you. Enter in. And may you safely, at the ending of your journey, return this way again.'

Gilgamesh entered in. He took the road that the Sun God walks at midnight while men sleep. The first league, there was darkness and no light before him or behind; the second league, thick was the darkness and there was no light before him or behind; and at the eighth league, Gilgamesh cried out, for there was darkness still, and still no light before him or behind. But at the ninth, he felt the North Wind blow upon his face; at the eleventh he saw light; and after twelve came out into the sun.

He came into the garden of the sun, where Shamash walks at evening, where each leaf is made of lapis lazuli, where vines bear dark carnelians. It was there that Shamash saw him and his heart was troubled.

'No living man has passed this way,' he said, 'nor will again, and you will never find what you are looking for, while this world lasts, because the gods decreed that darkness be the end of mortal life.'

Gilgamesh answered: 'Should I rest my head in the midst of earth and sleep for all the years when I have come so far? Should I stay here? I must go on. But let me see the sun, though I am as a dead man in this place, far from the land of living. Let me look, till I can look no longer, at its fire, for there is only darkness after death.'

Down by the shore of the sea, there was a house where sat Siduri, Woman of the Vine, using the golden jug and golden vat the gods had given her, to make their wine. When she looked up, she saw a man approach and, even from a distance, she could see that, though he had the stature of a god, despair was in his heart, and on his face was the look of one who travelled without hope. She took counsel with herself.

'Surely,' she said, 'this man must be a murderer who comes here. Why else should he be wandering in this place?'

She barred her gate. Gilgamesh heard the heavy bolt shoot home. He said: 'Siduri, what was it you saw that made you bar your gate? Do you not know that I am Gilgamesh, who killed Humbaba, cut the cedar down, and seized and slew the Bull that came from Heaven?'

Siduri said: 'If *you* are Gilgamesh, who killed Humbaba, cut the cedar down, and seized and slew the Bull that came from Heaven, why are your cheeks so thin, why are they burnt with cold and heat, why do you wander in the desert and the plain? Why is despair within your heart and on your face the look of one who travels without hope?'

He said to her: 'Why should these things not be? My friend, my younger brother, who once ran with the wild ass and the panther of the plain, who ascended mountains with me, killed the Bull and slew Humbaba, keeper of the trees; my friend whom I loved dearly, and who went beside me through all hardships—he is dead. The fate of man has overtaken him. For seven days and seven nights I wept, and would not give him up for burial, thinking "My friend will rise at my lament." But the Annunaki, Judges of the Dead, seized him. He is gone, and now my life is empty, so I roam the grassy plains and deserts, far and wide. How can I be silent, when my friend, my younger brother whom I loved, has turned to clay? And I, shall I not like him soon lie down and never rise again? I am afraid.'

'Gilgamesh, where are you running? You will never find what you are looking for while this world lasts, because the gods decreed that darkness be the end of mortal life. And you, great King, must learn to live your life from day to day, and look no further than the evening's rest. Short pleasures can be sweet. Take food and wine, be merry and rejoice. Go now again the way you came, return to your dear wife and to the child that holds you by the hand, for love was granted men as well as death.'

'I loved my brother Enkidu. He died. How can I rest, when I must die as he? Tell me the road to Utnapishtim. O, tell me how to find him! I will cross the sea and if I cannot cross, roam in the desert waste, for I have heard that he alone has everlasting life. He will tell me how to win it for myself.'

Siduri said: 'No man has ever crossed. None who has come here since the days of old has crossed the sea, save Shamash in his course. Hard is the passage; bitter, dark and deep are the Waters of Death that bar the way to land, that flow between the sea and Dilmun's shore. But Gilgamesh, go down into the

woods, and look for Urshanabi. He is there, close by the Images of Stone which keep him safe as Utnapishtim's Boatman. It may be that he will take you over, but if not, turn back, go home. There is no other way.'

Gilgamesh grew fretful at her words and went down to the edges of the sea. With his axe he struck, in senseless rage, the Images of Stone that stood nearby and shattered them. He then walked further on and came upon the Boatman in the woods, as he was carving a new prow. He rose and said: 'My name is Urshanabi. Who are you?'

'Do you not know that I am Gilgamesh, who killed Humbaba, cut the cedar down, and seized and slew the Bull that came from Heaven?'

The Boatman said: 'If *you* are Gilgamesh, who killed Humbaba, cut the cedar down, and seized and slew the Bull that came from Heaven, why are your cheeks so thin, why are they burnt with cold and heat, why do you wander in the desert and the plain? Why is despair within your heart and on your face the look of one who travels without hope?'

He said to him: 'Why should these things not be? My friend,

my younger brother, who once ran with the wild ass and the panther of the plain, who ascended mountains with me, killed the Bull and slew Humbaba, keeper of the trees; my friend whom I loved dearly, and who went beside me through all hardships—he is dead. The fate of man has overtaken him. For seven days and seven nights I wept and would not give him up for burial, thinking: "My friend will rise again at my lament." But the Annunaki seized him. He has gone, and now my life is empty, so I roam the grassy plains and deserts, far and wide. How can I be silent, when my friend, my younger brother whom I loved, has turned to clay? And I, shall I not like him soon lie down and never rise again? I am afraid. So take me to Utnapishtim! Ferry me across, for he alone has everlasting life and will tell me how to win it for myself.'

Urshanabi said: 'We cannot go. You broke the Images of Stone that kept me safe. The passage is now dangerous—but yet go down into the woods, and with your axe cut out a hundred and twenty poles; each one must be full sixty cubits long. We may yet cross.'

Gilgamesh went at once into the woods and cut the poles, in number and in size just as the Boatman said. They launched the boat and glided on the sea, and in three days had made a journey of six weeks. When they had crossed the sea, they ran at last into the Waters of Death that barred the way to land, and flowed between the sea and Dilmun's shore. Then Urshanabi said: 'Take up a pole and thrust it deep. Now cast the thing away, for it is wet to almost its full length. You must not touch the Waters with your hands or you will die. Now take a second up, and now a third, a fourth, a fifth, a sixth, a seventh, an eighth.'

Gilgamesh pushed the boat on with the poles until the last

E   65

was used, but still they were far out upon the Waters, far from land. So then the King stood up and spread his arms, and with his garment for a sail they reached the shore.

The Flower of Youth

Utnapishtim, called the Faraway, was sitting at his ease upon the slopes of Dilmun, in the Garden of the Gods, and when he saw the boat come in to land, he took counsel with himself, and in his heart said: 'Who has destroyed the Images of Stone that used to guard the ship? Who is this man who comes here with my boatman on the sea? He is none of mine!'

As they approached, he called: 'Who are you, and what is it you seek, that you have crossed such waters on your way?'

'Do you not know that I am Gilgamesh, who killed Humbaba, cut the cedar down, and seized and slew the Bull that came from Heaven?'

Utnapishtim said: 'If *you* are he, who killed Humbaba, cut the cedar down, and seized and slew the Bull that came from Heaven, why are your cheeks so thin, why are they burnt with cold and heat, why do you wander in the desert and the plain? Why is despair within your heart and on your face the look of one who travels without hope?'

He answered him: 'Why should these things not be? My friend, my younger brother who once ran with the wild ass and the panther of the plain, who ascended mountains with me, killed the Bull and slew Humbaba, keeper of the trees; my friend whom I loved dearly, and who went beside me through all hardships—he is dead. The fate of man has overtaken him. For seven days and seven nights I wept,

66

and would not give him up for burial, thinking: "My friend will rise at my lament." But the Annunaki, Judges of the Dead, seized him. He is gone, and now my life is empty, so I roam the grassy plains and deserts, far and wide. How can I be silent when my friend, my younger brother whom I loved, has turned to clay? And I, shall I not like him soon lie down and never rise again? I am afraid.'

'Gilgamesh, where are you running? You will never find what you are looking for while this world lasts, because the gods decreed that darkness be the end of mortal life. For do we build a house to last for ever, make a law to last for ever— from the days of old there is no permanence. The river brings a flood but then it falls; the sun comes out then hides behind a cloud; the gods allotted life but also death. How like they are—the sleeping and the dead; both picture death, a lesser and a great. Sleep is the sign of your mortality.'

'I have crossed mountains, I have crossed the seas and never had my fill of restful sleep. I was wearied out with walking and my clothing hung in rags before I reached Siduri of the Vine. I have killed the lion and tiger, the bear, the panther and the stag, the ibex and hyena, and the creatures of the plain, to eat their flesh and wear their skins, since I set out to find you. For you alone can tell me how to win immortal life, life everlasting. *You* look like a man, you are no different from myself, and yet you live. In my heart I thought that you would seem a god, a mighty man of battle—here you lie idly on your side out in the sun! Tell me how you got the precious gift of everlasting life and entered into the company of the gods.'

Utnapishtim said: 'I will reveal a hidden thing, a secret of the gods, and tell how Ea saved me from the Flood.'

He told him how the gods had drowned the world, but for his piety had taken him to live for ever in fair Dilmun.

'As for you,' he said, 'what can we do to help you win this life for which you seek? First, we must see if you can pass the test and overcome the little death of sleep. Six days and seven nights you must not sleep.'

But Gilgamesh had walked the desert waste and he was weary; sleep came falling down, sleep like a rainstorm blew on him; he slept.

Utnapishtim said: 'Look at the man who thought that he could win eternal life! Sleep like a rainstorm blows on him; he sleeps, and sleeping proves he is no more than man. Did I not say the sleeping and the dead both picture death? Wife, see him where he lies! If Gilgamesh cannot even conquer sleep, a little dying, how much less shall he withstand its image, true death, when it comes.'

Utnapishtim's wife said: 'Touch the man that he may awake, that he may now return upon the road by which he came, to his own land.'

'Deceitful is mankind! This man will try to deceive us by

denying that he slept. We must give him proof. Therefore
bake loaves of bread and each day stand a fresh one by his head
to mark the passing time as he sleeps on.'

So she baked loaves of bread and every day stood one beside
the King, till the day came when the first was hard as stone, the
third still moist, the sixth one freshly baked, the seventh
unmade. Then Utnapishtim touched the sleeping man and he
awoke.

'I hardly slept,' he said.

'Count up the loaves and see how many days.'

'Where shall I go now, and what shall I do? Wherever I
set my foot, death comes behind! For if I cannot even conquer
sleep, a little dying, how much less shall I be able to withstand its image, death?'

Utnapishtim told his Boatman that he must take the King
down to the washing-place to bathe him and to cleanse his
matted hair.

'And I will give him garments such that they will show
no sign of wear until he comes into Uruk again. You must go
with him; since you brought him here, across the boundaries
of life and death, and broke the rule established by the gods,
you cannot stay, you can no longer be my Boatman. Urshanabi,
you must leave.'

Urshanabi did as he was told and when the King was washed
and clothed anew, they launched the boat to make the
journey back. But Utnapishtim's wife said: 'Gilgamesh was
weary when he came and weary goes. What will you give him
now for all his pains, to take back to his land?'

So Utnapishtim called to them; the King took up a pole
and brought the boat back in towards the bank.

'Gilgamesh, you were weary when you came and weary go.

What would you have of me for all your pains, to take back to your land? I will reveal to you a hidden thing, a secret of the gods, so listen well. Beneath the waters in a certain place there grows a little plant with spines as sharp as any thorn or rose. If you can pluck it, then your hands will hold the Flower of Youth, to make you young again.'

Utnapishtim told him where to look and, with the Boatman, Gilgamesh set out. When they reached the place that they were looking for, Gilgamesh tied stones upon his feet and leapt into the waters. Down and down, into the deepest channels of the sea he sank, and there he saw the plant. He grasped its stem; although it pricked his hands, he plucked it from its roots, cut off the stones, and let the waters bear him to the light.

He said to Urshanabi: 'See this plant. It is the Flower of Youth, and by its power old men grow young again. I will return to Uruk and there give this magic plant to all the old to eat and at the last, when I have reached old age, I too shall eat and have back all my strength.'

So Gilgamesh and Urshanabi sailed over the sea towards

Uruk again, and after fifty leagues they stopped to rest because the night had come. They pulled to shore. There was a pool of cool, clean water near, and Gilgamesh the King went down to bathe, leaving the Flower of Youth upon the bank. But deep down in the pool, a serpent lay that smelled the Flower. It rose up, seized it, ate. It sloughed its skin, becoming young again.

Then Gilgamesh sat down and wept aloud: 'Was it for this that I have laboured? Has the life-blood of my heart been spent all for a serpent? This my prize? Though everlasting life could not be mine, yet in my hand I held the Flower of Youth. Now I have lost it there is nothing left.

'Come with me, Urshanabi, to Uruk; let us leave the boat and make our way by land. I will show you my great city. There at least, my toil has not been fruitless. Its high walls and the ramparts I have raised—these things will be all there is left of me when I am dead.'

So Gilgamesh the golden, King of Kings, resigned himself to death, the fate of men. He came back weary from his wandering and wrote on brick this tale of ancient days. Though he was mortal man, he set his name where great men's names were set, and where no names were, there he built an altar to the gods.

4. Adapa and the South Wind

This is the story of Adapa, the priest-king of Eridu, the most ancient city in Babylonia. Adapa was said to be the son of Ea, the god of the sweet waters and of wisdom, and the patron of Eridu. He served as priest in his father's temple, which meant that he also acted as steward, providing the god with food and drink. The idea that the gods were actually fed by the sacrifices made by men recurs in Marduk and Tiamat, *where the main reason for the creation of mankind is that men will be able to relieve the defeated gods of the burdensome task of feeding their victorious brothers.*

Like Gilgamesh, Adapa loses a great gift of the gods through no real fault of his own. Is it accident that Ea warns him against the bread of death, but does not mention the bread of life? Can we believe that the god of wisdom, 'who knows all things', did not foresee this offer of eternal life? Probably he misled Adapa quite deliberately: he had not made his son immortal when he created him and saw no reason to change his mind. In this case, the story would resemble legends such as that of Prometheus, in which the gods, jealous of their special attributes, will not share them with aspiring man.

The story of Adapa has been preserved on four clay tablets. One was found among the archives of the Egyptian kings Amenhotep III and IV and dates from about the first half of the fourteenth century BC, *while the others came from the library of Ashurbanipal, like the* Epic of Gilgamesh *and* Enuma elish.

To Adapa, his son, Ea the All-knowing had given wisdom

beyond measure; he had disclosed to him the secret lore of heaven and earth; he had created him the model of all men; yet he had not bestowed the most precious gift of all, eternal life, but left him mortal man. Adapa was the priest and the fisherman of Ea and each day at the bright quay, the Quay of the New Moon, he boarded his sailing-boat to catch fish for his master.

One day, the boat was running before the wind out on the wide sea and Adapa was steering with an oar, as best he could, when the South Wind came and sank the boat. It sent Adapa spinning down into the deeps, the realm of Ea. He rose up, gasping, and cried out: 'South Wind! I will break your wing!'

Just as Adapa said this, the South Wind's wing *was* broken, by the word, perhaps, of Ea, taking vengeance for his priest.

For seven days the South Wind did not blow upon the land, and Anu, Lord of Heaven, called to his messenger: 'Ilabrat, can *you* tell me? Where has the South Wind gone to? Why has he not blown on the land these seven days?'

'My lord, Adapa, son of Ea, is to blame, for he has broken the wing of the South Wind so that he cannot fly.'

When Anu heard, he was enraged and, rising from his throne, cried out: 'Go! Fetch Adapa to me!'

But Ea, who knows all things, heard Anu's words in Heaven and, summoning Adapa, gave him this advice: 'My son, put on a mourning-robe. You are going before Anu. You will take the road to Heaven and, when you have gone up, you will approach the Gate of Anu. Tammuz and Gizzida, the gods who die and are reborn, will be standing at the gate. They will ask you: "Man, who is it for that you look thus? Who is it for that you wear the robe of mourning?" You must say: "From our land two gods have disappeared. It is for them that I look thus."

' "What gods are they?"

' "Tammuz and Gizzida, the gods who die and are reborn."

'They will glance then at each other and they will smile with pleasure. Their hearts will be won and they will come with you to speak a kindly word to Anu. They will assuage his wrath and he will look on you with favour. And yet you must beware. As you stand before his throne he will command the gods to offer you the bread of death: you must not eat. As you stand before his throne, he will command the gods to offer you the water of death: you must not drink. As you stand before his throne, he will command the gods to offer you a garment, and that you may put on. Likewise you may anoint yourself with the oil that they will bring. Heed my advice, Adapa. Do not neglect my words.'

The messenger of Anu came to Eridu and said: 'The lord Anu, King of Heaven, has commanded me to come here and fetch to him Adapa, who broke the South Wind's wing.'

He made Adapa take the road to Heaven and he climbed it. When he had ascended, he went up to the fence and saw Tammuz and Gizzida beside the Gate of Anu. When they saw

Adapa, the two dead gods cried out: 'Man, who is it for that you look thus? Who is it for that you wear the robe of mourning?'

Adapa answered: 'From our land two gods have disappeared. It is for them that I look thus.'

'What gods are they?'

'Tammuz and Gizzida, the gods who die and are reborn.'

They glanced then at each other, and they both smiled with pleasure. Their hearts were won and they went with him before Lord Anu's throne. When Anu saw Adapa drawing near, he cried out: 'Come here, Adapa. Tell me true. Why did you break the South Wind's wing?'

'My lord,' Adapa answered, 'I was fishing for my master, catching fish for the table of Ea, my father, and the sea was like a mirror. But the South Wind came and sank my boat. It sent me spinning down into the deeps, the realm of Ea. In the anger of my heart I cried out against the wind: "South Wind! I will break your wing!" And even as I did so, the South Wind's wing was broken.'

Then Tammuz and Gizzida spoke up at his side and defended him to Anu. Anu's anger was appeased and his heart grew quiet as they coaxed his wrath away. He said: 'Now why did Ea give such wisdom to a human? Why did he disclose the secret lore of heaven and earth and create him the model of all men, and yet leave him still a mortal man when all is said and done? As for us, here in Heaven, now what shall *we* do for him? Fetch him the bread of life, that he may eat.'

The bread was fetched but, mindful of the word of Ea, Adapa did not eat. The water of life was fetched but, mindful of the word of Ea, Adapa did not drink. A garment was fetched and he put it on, and anointed himself with the oil that they brought in.

Anu looked on, and laughed.

'Come here, Adapa. Tell me true. Why did you not eat or drink?'

'It was Ea, Lord of Wisdom, who commanded that I should not.'

'Of all the gods of heaven and earth, as many as there be, who would give such a command? You have refused eternal life! What god would set his own decree above my word—to say "you must not eat" when *I* give bread; to say "you must not drink" when *I* give water! The command of Anu is over all; hearken to no other. Remain a mortal man and doomed to die. Take him away! Return him to the earth!'

So Adapa was taken back to earth, and lived his days out as a mortal man, for the gift of eternal life, when once refused, could not be offered again. But Anu took pity on him and to comfort his distress made him famous among men and for Adapa's sake sent Ninkarrak the Healer down to earth—Ninkarrak the goddess whose cool hand drives fever out and soothes away all pain and helps men bear their own mortality.

76

5. Inanna in the Underworld

The tablets on which this poem are written were excavated at Nippur, and they were inscribed in about 2000 BC. This story is the only one of our collection taken straight from a Sumerian text, and it needs a special word of explanation. All the other stories, though Sumerian in origin, reach us in the form in which the Babylonians told them, and contain the alterations made by the Babylonians themselves. Because of this, it does not matter if we always refer to the Water God as Ea; though the Babylonians knew him by many names, their idea of him was the same. But I have not felt justified in giving the characters in this story the names of their Babylonian counterparts. Though it may be true that the Babylonian Ishtar was at first identical with the Sumerian love-goddess, Inanna, the Babylonian priests seem to have tried to make her a little less formidable. For they took the story which follows and reversed it. The cult of Tammuz as a vegetation-god became very popular in late Babylonian times, and the old myth of Inanna in the Underworld *was altered to fit it. Ishtar was made to rescue the shepherd Tammuz from the underworld, to represent the return of spring to the world, as in the Greek story of Persephone. Some Babylonians still knew the old story, of course. In the* Epic of Gilgamesh, *the hero reproaches Ishtar with having caused the death of Tammuz. But the priests would not have encouraged the continued belief in this myth, and we must avoid the error of believing that what the Babylonians thought about Ishtar was the same as what the Sumerians thought about Inanna. For this reason, I am preserving the Sumerian names throughout. I have not included the names in the glossary, but here*

77

are the Sumerian forms with their later Babylonian equivalents:

Sumerian: *Inanna*	Babylonian: *Ishtar*
Dumuzi	*Tammuz*
Enki	*Ea*
Utu	*Shamash*

INANNA, the Goddess of Love, and the mighty Queen of Heaven turned her mind from the realm of the air to the realm of darkness below, and coveted the kingdom of her sister, Ereshkigal. The Lady abandoned Heaven and she abandoned

Earth and went down into the Underworld, the Kingdom of the Dead. She first put on a breastplate and a royal garment. She took the seven laws of the gods and hung them at her side, the sceptre of lapis lazuli and held it in her hand, the Crown of the Plain and set it on her head. A necklace of lapis lazuli she wound about her neck, on her breast pinned two bright jewels, slipped a gold ring on her hand. And thus attired, Inanna walked in state down into the Underworld, the Kingdom of the Dead. At her side was Ninshubur, her messenger.

She said to him: 'Go, Ninshubur, my true support and my faithful messenger. I am now descending into the Underworld. When I have gone into the darkness, set up a wailing for me, let the drums sound in my shrine, and in the temples of the gods do you wander like a poor man, dressed in but a single garment. First you must go to Nippur, into the house of Enlil. To the dwelling of the Air God you must make your way alone. Upon entering the temple, you must cry: "O, father Enlil, let not your daughter, fair Inanna, be put to death down in the dark." And if he will not help you, you must go next unto Ur, into the house of Nanna. To the dwelling of the Moon God you must make your way alone. Upon entering the temple, you must cry: "O, father Nanna, let not your daughter, fair Inanna, be put to death down in the dark." And if he will not help you, you must go to Eridu, into the house of Enki. To the dwelling of the Water God you must make your way alone. Upon entering the temple, you must cry: "O, father Enki, let not your daughter, fair Inanna, be put to death down in the dark." And Father Enki, Lord of Wisdom, will bring me back to life.'

Then Inanna spoke again to her messenger: 'Go, Ninshubur. Do what I have commanded. Do not neglect my word.'

When Inanna arrived at the door into the Underworld, she spoke proudly to the Keeper: 'Unlock the door, for I would enter!'

'Who, pray, are *you?*' asked Neti.

'I am the Queen of Heaven, where the sun shines,' said Inanna.

'If you are the Queen of Heaven, why have you come down *here?* What strong desire has led you from the world in which the sun shines, into the land of no return, along the path which none walks twice?'

'I have come to see my sister, Ereshkigal,' said Inanna.

'Wait here, Inanna,' Neti said. 'I must go and ask the Queen.'

The Keeper hurried down into the house of Ereshkigal, and he said: 'O my Queen, there is a maiden at the gate. She wears a breastplate and a royal robe, the laws of the gods hang at her side, the sceptre of lapis lazuli is in her hand, upon her head the Crown of the Plain is set. She wears a necklace of lapis lazuli, two jewels on her breast, and a gold ring on her hand. She would come in.'

Ereshkigal grew more angry as he listed each adornment, for she knew it was Inanna who had come, in all her state, to challenge her authority.

'Neti, I command you to unbolt the seven gates of the Kingdom of the Dead and set wide the doors of Ganzir, my great palace. I command you that she shall be brought in naked. Upon her entering in, she shall be made to bow before my throne.'

Neti the doorkeeper heeded Ereshkigal and drew back the bolts on the seven heavy gates. The creaking doors of Ganzir he swung back on mighty hinges.

'Come, Inanna. Enter.'

Upon her entering in, the Crown of the Plain was taken from her head.

'What are you doing?' said Inanna.

'Be silent, proud Inanna. It is the ancient custom of the Kingdom of the Dead.'

At the second gate he took from her the rod of lapis lazuli, and at the third the necklace that was wound about her neck. At the fourth, he took the jewels and at the fifth, the golden ring. At the sixth, he took the breastplate and, when the seventh gate was reached, Inanna's royal garment was taken from her body. She was brought naked to the palace and there made to bow down low before the throne of Ereshkigal. The seven Judges of the Underworld, the fearful Annunaki, pronounced their judgment on Inanna: the Queen of Heaven must die. Ereshkigal spoke the word of wrath that condemned Inanna. She turned the eye of death on her. Inanna was a corpse, and dry and light as any leaf. They hung her from a nail.

When three days and three nights had passed, Ninshubur the messenger set up a wailing for Inanna, let the drums sound in her shrine, and in the temples of the gods he wandered, in a single garment, as the goddess had commanded. First, he went to Nippur, into the house of Enlil. To the dwelling of the Air God he made his way alone. Upon entering the temple, he wept.

'O, father Enlil, let not your daughter, fair Inanna, be put to death down in the dark. Let not Inanna die!'

But Enlil would not help him, so he went next unto Ur, into the house of Nanna. To the dwelling of the Moon God he made his way alone. Upon entering the temple, he wept.

'O, father Nanna, let not your daughter, fair Inanna, be put to death down in the dark. Let not Inanna die!'

But Nanna would not help him, so he went to Eridu, into the house of Enki. To the dwelling of the Water God he made his way alone. Upon entering the temple, he wept.

'O, father Enki, let not your daughter, fair Inanna, be put to death down in the dark. Let not Inanna die!'

And Enki answered Ninshubur: 'What has happened to my daughter? I am troubled in my heart for her.' Ninshubur told the tale. When he had finished, Enki cleaned his finger-nails;

from his red-painted finger-nails the great god took out dirt and from it made two creatures, Kurgarru and Kalaturru. The water of life and the bread of life he gave unto their care. Enki told them: 'Go with haste down into the Underworld. Before the throne of Ereshkigal you will be offered gifts. They will offer you the water that comes out of the river. Do not drink it; do not eat the grain they bring you from the fields. But say to Ereshkigal, the fearful Queen of Darkness: "We want no gifts except the corpse that hangs there, on the nail." When the corpse is given you, sprinkle on it what you carry, the water and the bread of life: then will Inanna live.'

The two went down into the darkness. Before the throne of Ereshkigal they were offered water from the river, but they would not drink. They were offered grain, but they would not eat of it.

'We want no gifts except the corpse that hangs there, on the nail.'

Ereshkigal answered: 'It is your Queen's corpse.'

'We still would have it.'

The body of Inanna was taken from the nail. The Kurgarru sprinkled bread on it, the Kalaturru sprinkled water. The corpse rose up before them, Inanna rose, and lived. Ereshkigal was enraged at the trick the gods had played, and when the Queen of Heaven made to leave the Underworld, the Annunaki seized her.

'Who has gone from here unharmed when once they have descended? If you would go, you must send back another in your place.'

Inanna said that she would send a life to pay for her life, and a pack of demons went with her to bring her ransom back. Those who ascended with Inanna needed neither food nor water;

spirits shaped like reeds, they were the demons of disease who take the wife from her dear husband, the child from its dear mother. They ran beside Inanna as she walked up from the dark. When she came into the sunshine, Ninshubur, her messenger, threw himself down at her feet and lay there in the dust. The demons cried: 'Inanna! We will take him as your ransom.'

The Queen of Heaven answered: 'No. He is my messenger, who neither fails nor falters. He filled Heaven with his wailing and caused the drums to beat. He wandered in the temples, clad in but a single garment. He went to Nippur and to Ur and to Eridu for me. In Eridu, he went into the house of Father Enki; he wept before the god and Enki brought me back to life.'

The demons said: 'Then let us run before Inanna into Umma; let us run into the temple and there seize upon the god.'

But when they came to Umma, the god Shara knelt before her; he lay down in the dusty road before Inanna's feet. The demons cried: 'Inanna! We will take him as your ransom.'

But Inanna would not let him go, because he had bowed down.

'Let us run before Inanna into Badtibira; let us run into the temple and there seize upon the gods.'

But when they came to Badtibira, the gods knelt down before her; they lay down in the dusty road before Inanna's feet.

The demons cried: 'Inanna! We will take them as your ransom.'

But Inanna would not let them go, because they had bowed down.

'Let us run before Inanna into Kullab, to the temple, and there seize upon Dumuzi, the husband of the Queen.'

To greet his wife, Dumuzi had dressed in royal garments and, as he sat high on his throne, the demons seized on him. They could not reach more than his thigh, so lofty was his chair. Because he had not bowed to her, Inanna spoke the word of wrath, condemning him to die: 'And as for that one—take him!'

She turned on him the eye of death. The demons seized on him, demons who kiss sick children and take the man's son from his knee. Into their hands Inanna gave his life to buy her own. Dumuzi wept. His face grew pale. He raised his arms toward the Sun God and he prayed: 'O Utu, my wife's brother, hear me now. Turn my hand to a snake's hand. Turn my foot to a snake's foot. Let not the demons seize me. Let me slither from their grasp!'

But he did not escape the demons. He was led down into darkness, to the house of Ereshkigal in the Kingdom of the Dead.

About the Author

JENNIFER WESTWOOD studied at St. Anne's College, Oxford, and at New Hall, Cambridge. She has taught at Cambridge and is concluding research for her PhD thesis on medieval Icelandic romances.

Jennifer Westwood has traveled extensively in Europe and has studied in France, Denmark, Sweden and Iceland. At present, her home is London.

An earlier book, *Medieval Tales,* was published recently by Coward-McCann.

ACKNOWLEDGEMENT AND BIBLIOGRAPHY

Acknowledgement and Bibliography

My thanks are due to Dr E. Sollberger of the British Museum, who directed me to transliterations in the following:

Alexander Heidel, *The Gilgamesh Epic and Old Testament Parallels*, University of Chicago, 1946.

Alexander Heidel, *The Babylonian Genesis*, University of Chicago, 1942.

S. N. Kramer, *Sumerian Mythology*, American Philosophic Society, Philadelphia, 1944.

J. B. Pritchard, *Ancient Near Eastern Texts Relating to the Old Testament*, Princeton, 1950.

A concise account of the Flood-material and how it was deciphered is: Edmund Sollberger, *The Babylonian Legend of the Flood*, The British Museum, Second Edition, 1966.

ACKNOWLEDGEMENT AND BIBLIOGRAPHY

The illustrations on pages 7, 89 and 93 are based on the following archaeological remains: page 7, cylinder seal and impression, Middle East, *c.* 3200 BC; page 89, bowl, Bakur, *c.* 3500 BC, beaker, Susa, *c.* 3000 BC; page 93, gaming board, Ur, *c.* 3500 BC.

GLOSSARY

Glossary

Adad The storm god.

Annunaki The Judges of the Dead, who resided in the Babylonian Underworld.

Anshan A district of Elam in South-west Persia, probably the source of wood for especially good bows.

Anshar From the mingling of Apsu and Tiamat were produced first Lahmu and his female counterpart Lahamu, then Anshar and his partner Kishar. It is uncertain what these four represent. Anshar was the father of Anu.

Anu The son of Anshar, Anu was the sky god. He is often referred to as King of Heaven or Father of the Gods. The 'decree of Anu' was fate.

Apsu The primeval sweet-water ocean, personified as a god. 'The Apsu' denotes the home of Ea, built on the back of the defeated Apsu, that is, his home floated on the sweet waters which were thought to lie under the earth and feed the fresh-water springs in the earth.

Dilmun The Garden of the Gods, a sort of Paradise, reserved

93

for the use of Utnapishtim and his wife. When Gilgamesh speaks of 'everlasting life' he means the immortality that Utnapishtim enjoys, not the life-after-death of Christianity. In Babylonian belief, Heaven was for the gods alone. For the dead, whether good or bad, there was only the realm of Ereshkigal, Queen of the Underworld, the place of darkness described by Enkidu. It is because 'darkness is the end of mortal life' that Gilgamesh wants so desperately to find the secret of Utnapishtim's immortality.

Ea The god of the sweet waters in and under the earth, who built his home on Apsu, the primeval ocean, after conquering him. As the god of drinking-water, he is generally regarded as benevolent. His treatment of Adapa seems rather shabby, but was probably in the best interests of the gods. He was the patron of Eridu, on the Persian Gulf. When Utnapishtim is instructed to tell people that he is going down to dwell with Ea in the Apsu, the reference is probably to the marshy region around Eridu.

Enlil The god of earth and sky, the region between the Apsu ruled by Ea, and Heaven ruled by Anu. He was the supreme god of Babylonia until Marduk replaced him. The creation-myth contained in *Enuma elish* was probably related with Enlil as the central figure until the rise of Marduk. He is still the chief god in the *Story of the Flood*. Enlil was the patron of Nippur.

Ereshkigal The sister of Ishtar and the Queen of the Under-world.

Ishtar The goddess of love and war, sometimes called the Queen of Heaven. Some thought her the daughter of Anu, others of Nanna. She was notorious for her fickleness in love and on this ground was rejected by Gilgamesh, in whose city of Uruk she had her chief temple. She was the wife of Tammuz and in Sumerian belief seems to have betrayed him to his death, though in later Babylonian stories, she brought him back from the Underworld.

Marduk The son of Ea, he was elevated to the position of national god of Babylonia during the First Babylonian Dynasty (1894-1595 BC). He replaced Enlil as the leader of the gods and was credited with the defeat of Tiamat and the creation of the world, both of which were probably feats of Enlil.

Mashu If this word is Babylonian, it may mean 'twins', and refer to a twin-peaked mountain. It is the name of the mountain into which the sun passes at night. While it was dark, the sun god was believed to be in his own garden beyond Mashu. At dawn he returned to the world through the mountain, the gate of which was guarded by the Scorpion-man and his mate, mythical monsters half-human, half-scorpion.

Nanna The moon god and patron of Ur. Perhaps the father of Ishtar.

Ninkarrak The goddess of healing.

Ninsun The mother of Gilgamesh, she was a minor goddess resident in Egalmah, the 'Great Palace', of Uruk.

Nisir Mount Nisir, on which Utnapishtim's ark came to rest, has been identified with Pir Omar Gudrun, a mountain 8,600 feet high, east of the River Tigris.

Samuqan The cattle god, who is said to have had a shaggy hide like a wild ox.

Shamash The sun god, who hated darkness and evil and is represented as a champion of Justice.

Tammuz Like his father Gizzida, he was a vegetation-god who died with the plants in the winter, but revived with them in the spring. Babylonian liturgies suggest that his wife Ishtar rescued him from the Underworld. According to the writer of the *Epic of Gilgamesh*, however, she betrayed him as she betrayed other lovers. The poet may have known the Sumerian story of *Inanna in the Underworld*. In his role of vegetation-god, Tammuz was known to the prophet Ezekiel, who mentions the women's custom of wailing for Tammuz (Ezekiel viii : 14).

Tiamat The primeval salt-water ocean, personified as a goddess, and the wife of Apsu.

Uruk One of the city-states of Sumer, it lay between Babylon and Ur. Its biblical name is Erech. Archaeological excavation has shown that it was an important city from early times. It contained large temples for the worship of Anu and Ishtar, and was the seat of a line of kings of whom the fifth was Gilgamesh.